Do my story, sing my song

Do my story, sing my song

Music therapy and Playback Theatre with troubled children

✧

Jo Salas

Tusitala Publishing

Do my story, sing my song:
Music therapy and Playback Theatre with troubled children

Copyright © 2007 Jo Salas

Tusitala Publishing
137 Hasbrouck Road
New Paltz, NY 12561
USA

www.tusitalapublishing.com

Chapter 6, "Do My Story!" was previously published in English and Chinese by Arts with the Disabled Association, Hong Kong, in *Chorus,* 2005.

Chapter 10, "Stories from the Space Room," was previously published by Charles C Thomas in *Current Approaches in Drama Therapy,* editors Lewis and Johnson, in 2000.

Book design: Carol Hanisch, Word/Graphics.
wordgraphics@verizon.net

Cover photo: Elise Gold

ISBN 978-0-9642350-6-9

Printed in the United States of America.
5 4 3 2

For the children

"To restore the human subject at the centre—
the suffering, afflicted, fighting, human subject—
we must deepen a case history to a narrative or tale;
only then do we have a 'who' as well as a 'what,'
a real person...."

—Oliver Sacks, *The Man Who Mistook His Wife for a Hat*

CONTENTS

INTRODUCTION

Sylvia sat on the floor with a xylophone in front of her, her head down, face hidden. Tall for her eight years, she had big hands which could land a lightning punch when her rage, never far from the surface, was stirred.

"How're you doing today, Sylvia?" I asked her.

No response. Sylvia seldom looked at or spoke to anyone. Life so far had taught her that her fellow human beings were likely to be sources of pain or danger and she preferred to keep herself as removed as possible. I wanted to keep reaching out, but not just with words. "Would you like to play?"

More silence. I played a short phrase on the other xylophone and waited. Sylvia toyed with a mallet, then played a few notes. I played back, picking up the hints of rhythm in her phrase. A long pause. She played again, a mallet now in each hand. Slowly a musical dialogue grew. And then, suddenly, it was there—the connection between music-makers which is as unmistakable, as palpable, as richly communicative as holding hands or talking. Sylvia and I played and listened, listened and played, each responding to the other in the language of rhythm, melody, and harmony.

Our improvisation found its ending. Sylvia shot me one split-second look from her dark eyes before withdrawing again into solitude and her chosen silence. But we'd been somewhere together, and we could go there again.

Communicating with our fellow beings through the arts has been, as far as we know, a part of every human culture, past and present. The

Lascaut cave paintings, the fragile flute, aeons old, found recently in China, the central role of the arts in isolated contemporary cultures which may resemble our Stone Age past tell us that we humans have always been artists. We have always had the striving to find aesthetic form for perceptions and experiences too deep, too lofty, too intimate or elusive for communication in any other way. We need the arts to connect, to heal ourselves, to comprehend our lives and strive to fulfill them.

Even in technological, consumerist American culture—where the arts are relegated to the fringes or the elite, where arts-in-education programs in schools are eliminated or pressured to justify themselves in terms of higher academic test scores—the arts persist, vibrant, ingenious, and unbounded. Whatever their attitude toward the arts and artists, few people live without the enrichment of music and other art forms, even if passively and at a distance. There still are millions who actively seek out and value the work of professional artists in concerts, museums, and theatres, or become involved themselves as amateur musicians, painters, dancers, and so on. Others, impelled by the artist's calling, devote their lives to making art in one form or another, usually with little recompense or recognition.

We are born with the yearning to be creative, to synthesize elements from our surroundings and from them offer something to the world that embodies our understanding of it. Very young children do this by instinct and will continue to dance, sing, make up stories, paint pictures—until discouraged by parents or teachers, or distracted by television. Perhaps the hunger for new possessions—the quest that fills shopping malls every weekend—is in part the frustrated and unrecognized yearning to be creative. But the novelty of new clothes or gadgets is a poor substitute for the satisfaction of real creativity.

We also share a profound need for connection, for kinship and companionship; for the knowledge that we are not alone as we navigate the mysteries of our existence. The arts weave our lives with others, not only our contemporaries but our forebears. Through the arts we find and communicate meaning, reassurance, healing, vision: we move toward fulfilling ourselves, individually and as a society. "Creativity is the encounter of the intensively conscious human being with his or her world," says Rollo May in *The Courage to Create*.

The arts therapies—music, drama, art, dance—grew out of a recognition that art's particular capacity to inspire, connect, and heal could benefit adults and children suffering from mental or physical illness or other infirmity. If healthy people can find deep satisfaction, insight, comfort and inspiration in art, if they can express vision and emotion and join with others through the arts, then the arts could yield all this and more to ill or disabled people sorely in need of enrichment, connection, and meaning. Over the last sixty years—building on healing traditions going back to ancient times—artists in all media have joined with psychotherapists to develop methodologies that bring healing through the arts to people in need. In spite of the considerable skepticism, misunderstanding, and unfamiliarity that persist, the creative arts therapies are by now a well-established resource in medical and psychiatric hospitals, outpatient clinics, special education, programs for the disabled or elderly, rehabilitation, and so on.

Do my story, sing my song tells the stories of the silent Sylvia and a number of other young people who took part in music therapy and Playback Theatre (improvisation based on personal stories) at a residential treatment center for emotionally disturbed children where I worked for eleven years. The clinical director of the St Mary's Home for Children, finding some surplus funds at the end of one fiscal year, decided to try an experiment: what would happen if these seriously wounded children, the survivors of extreme neglect and abuse, were exposed to music and drama? He was an enthusiastic amateur musician himself and knew, as all musicians do, how playing music can "soothe the savage breast" and create bonds beyond language with listeners and fellow players. He hired me on the basis of my experience in music and Playback Theatre, in spite of my lack of therapeutic training at that point, and let me loose with very little in the way of either guidance or restrictions. I learned fast, taught mostly by the children themselves. After a couple years I sought formal training which led to a credential as a music therapist.

Over the years, I saw many of the children in individual music therapy sessions where they played and sang their tenderest feelings, their rages, their haunting fears. I led singing groups, trying to master the fine art of maintaining order. I taught the basics of Playback Theatre to other staff members and we performed for groups of the kids, who did not hesitate to tell their stories of sadness, triumph, and everyday revelation. They clearly relished the chance to be heard so fully and uncritically by staff as well as by the other children, a rare experience in the clamorous atmosphere of institutional life. Later I led groups where the children learned how to enact stories for each other, growing in empathy and self-confidence as they did so.

The book is a more-or-less chronological account of my experience at St Mary's, with chapters focusing especially on music therapy, others on Playback Theatre, and some that reflect on the story of developing a creative arts program alongside the more traditional modalities that everyone was used to. What I established at St Mary's was, of course, a reflection of my own abilities, interests, philosophical orientation, and personal experience. In some ways my program was similar to those at other treatment centers. In other ways it was distinct, especially in my use of Playback Theatre.

Even in my first years at St Mary's, when I barely knew what I was doing, the power of the arts themselves was unmistakable. For some of the children, the chance to find their core of strength and optimism as they made music or created theatre together was a potent part of their healing process. These were the luckier ones, whose wounds were not beyond repair, for whom treatment offered a chance to turn their lives in a new and better direction.

There were others to whom such grievous harm had been done that restoration to health and normality seemed unlikely, perhaps impossible. Yet over and over I witnessed the temporary transformation into wholeness that took place as the child's artistic self found expression. Even for these children—and perhaps especially for them—making music or theatre enabled them to feel the expansive power of creativity which is everyone's birthright.

The children at St Mary's were born as bright and beautiful, as full of promise as any other child. They were driven into mental illness by the events of their lives, in most cases compounded by the stresses and injustices of a harsh social order. By the time they were sent to St Mary's—there to stay for years, at least two, maybe four or five—many of them had been further hurt by their experiences in the foster care system, where all too often their problems had been exacerbated by mistreatment and repeated rejections. Some still had a parent or grandparent or aunt who welcomed them home for weekend visits; many had families who were far too troubled themselves to be a resource for their exiled child. Other children were effectively orphans, with parents who had surrendered their parental rights, or had had them terminated by the courts.

Disturbed though they certainly were—storm-tossed by turbulent emotion, prone to violence toward others and themselves, devoid of self-esteem or the simple conviction that they had a right to live—I found the children to be immensely spirited, dazzlingly creative. The longing to love and be loved burned in every one of them, no matter how buried or fearful that yearning might be. Their courage and endurance astonished and moved me. With few exceptions—the children who were already pulled toward psychosis or the sociopath's conscienceless life—they all had the potential to get better, if good fortune instead of tragedy could enter their lives for a change.

I'd known from my own personal experience that the arts can heal. Growing up with violence as well as privilege, it was music that redeemed my despair. Later, my work in Playback Theatre let me grow into myself. Working with the children at St Mary's taught me *how* the arts heal: through the opportunity for self-expression; through the success that a child may experience in the arts, engendering a sense of self-worth that nothing else in her life has ever promoted; through the opportunity to rebuild a damaged capacity for relationship and attachment; how the dreadful isolation suffered by many traumatized children can be mitigated, even transformed, when they join together in music and theatre. Faced with extreme cruelty or abandonment, children seize on anything that seems to promise safety or relief— running away, withdrawing, striking back, even self-destruction—and cling to these defenses even when they are no longer necessary or useful. The arts offered many of the St Mary's children an arena in which to discover new ways of relating to the world, unfettered by the desperate strategies they'd devised for sheer survival.

These effects, as well as others, are the basis of creative arts therapies. In addition, I was struck increasingly by a phenomenon that was little spoken about in the literature: the healing that comes directly from aesthetic experience itself. The artist, in a sense, is always creating order out of chaos: she or he brings elements together in an integrity of form which, to whatever degree the artist is capable, constitutes a message about the existence of order in an ontological sense. For children whose world has so far revealed nothing but fear and meaninglessness, this aesthetic effect is salutary indeed.

Being all that a human being can be has to do with the ability to connect compassionately to others; to communicate one's experience and be open to communication from others; and to draw on the god-like powers of imagination and creativity, the essential prerequisite to making change in one's life. In *Releasing the Imagination* the educator Maxine Greene says "the role of the imagination is...to awaken, to disclose the ordinarily unseen, unheard, unexpected....It is imagination that draws us on, that enables us to make new connections among parts of our experience, that suggests the contingency of the reality we are experiencing."

Involvement in the arts therapies also has the power to serve more pragmatic and measurable goals such as increasing attention span, improving social behavior, and enhancing academic performance. Important as these goals are, they should not obscure more fundamental reasons to take part in arts therapies, or in the arts themselves. The current proliferation of pre-school music programs for young children, for example, offers experiences that are deeply enriching and expanding in themselves regardless of whether they will help a child get into Harvard later on. All children need the arts in their lives, not in order to behave better or improve scores on academic tests, but for the same reasons that adults do: for the affirmation of beauty and meaning, for the cultivation of imagination and empathy.

My intention in this book is to tell stories which will bring some of the principles and processes of creative arts therapies to life, especially those of music therapy and Playback Theatre; and to introduce the remarkable children with whom it was my privilege to work. Although all the events that I describe here took place, I have at a few points telescoped time in the interests of the narrative. Dialogue is reconstructed from my notes and audiotapes, augmented by memory and imagination. A few of the characters are composites, though not the center stage ones. The names of all children and adults at St Mary's

Home for Children, and the name of the institution itself, are fictional, and some identifying details have been changed.

Because of the protections of the treatment system it was not possible for me to locate the children, now young adults, to consult them about telling their stories and, in some cases, quoting their compositions. My hope is that if they read *Do my story, sing my song* they will recognize the deep respect and affection with which it was written, as well as its potential benefits for other children in the future.

One

St Mary's

One of the stone pillars facing the road was set with a brass plaque: "St Mary's Home for Children," it said. I turned in toward an ivy-grown building with a steep-pitched slate roof glinting under late winter sun. There was a newer attachment on one side: a chapel, apparently, with bold stained-glass windows and life-size plaster saints on the patio in various attitudes of chagrin.

Inside the lobby a small man bustled up to me, smiling under an outsize moustache.

"Marcus Fisher," he said, grasping my hand. This was the clinical director who'd invited me for an interview. "Welcome to St Mary's." He gestured vaguely toward whatever lay beyond the lobby and the ornate sweep of the stairs. I followed him through a large, high-ceilinged living room with lace curtains and a fire place. I was impressed to see such a graceful room in an institution for children.

Through the door on the other side of the big room the decor changed abruptly. Linoleum floors, low ceilings, a fug of institutional food. In Dr Fisher's narrow office we talked about his vision for a program of music and drama for St Mary's seventy-five emotionally disturbed children and whether I was the right person to get it started. He seemed enthusiastic about my ideas, although I in fact knew little about working with children ill enough to be in residential treatment. I imagined small, deprived children, wan and unloved. I hoped I could help them.

"Would you like to look around?" said Dr Fisher after a while. By now, school was out—I'd learned that the kids lived fulltime under the capacious slate roof, attending an in-house school and going "home" at the end of the day to their living units upstairs or in the basement after playing outside on the blacktop or the sports fields, or exploring the stream and woods on St Mary's land. In the hallway, kids streamed by us like whitewater rapids. Some were the Dickensian waifs of my imagination but many were vigorous and big. They were mostly boys, half of them African-American. "Manny!" called Dr Fisher, catching the arm of a handsome curly-headed boy darting by. The boy cursed and squirmed violently out of his grasp. Dr Fisher laughed and shrugged. "I guess you'll have to meet Manny another time."

A month later, all formalities dealt with, I arrived for my first day of work. Dr Fisher led me across the playground to a cottage where a group of children lived with their caregivers on the first two floors. In the attic was a good-sized room, empty, with a wooden floor. I liked it. "I don't think this gets used much," he said. So the cottage attic became my domain, until it was taken over for offices a year later and I moved, eventually, to the Space Room.

I spent my first couple of days introducing myself to the staff, meeting the children, and setting up a schedule for groups and individual sessions. Neither Dr Fisher nor anyone else seemed concerned to help me get started—I was amazed at their trust, if that's what it was. Every day taught me more of the essentials. I soon realized, for example, why none of the therapists saw children in groups. With such wounded children you could spend all your time simply preventing them from hurting each other, or trying to get them to settle down enough to do something. My groups gradually diminished in size until I was seeing most of the children alone. On their own, the children were free to be their more private selves, vulnerable, creative, open to relationship.

"How's it going?" Dr Fisher called cheerily in the hallway a few weeks after I'd started.

"Good!" I said.

I was beginning to find my place. I learned that St Mary's complex organizational structure was reflected in its labyrinth of hallways and multiple stairways linking the three main floors. The basement was the home of the recreation department, a collection of independent-minded people who organized after-school and weekend activities and seemed to enjoy their work, in spite of their lowly position. Maintenance lived down there too, and the kitchen, sometimes the source of smells that turned my stomach but occasionally also a windfall of fresh-baked cookies offered generously over the half-door to lucky passers-by.

Another tunnel-like hallway led to classrooms for the youngest and noisiest children, with the rest of the school upstairs on the main floor. The teachers kept to themselves, with different hours from the other workers and different goals with the children: their main job was to impart basic academics, so that the children had some chance of holding their own with reading and math once they were back in the outside world.

The air became more rarefied as one climbed to the next floor, at least in the wing of the building which housed administrative offices and board rooms where financial and political decisions were made. Yet another flight of stairs led up to the private precinct of the nuns, the executive director and three or four other sisters. No one I knew had ever been invited up there. It was a realm as mysterious as Bertha Mason's attic, or heaven.

St Mary's was affiliated with the Archdiocese of New York, but in spite of the signs of Catholicism—the chapel, the religious pictures and statuary, the nuns in their traditional garb—there was a generally secular atmosphere. There were no prayers in school or in the living units. Religious instruction was offered only to the Catholic children or to Protestants whose parents had requested it. Funding was from state and federal sources, not the church.

The staff was divided between culturally conservative Catholics, fiercely iconoclastic lapsed Catholics, and liberal Jews. I seemed to be the only half-Protestant half-Jew with no religious affiliation whatever. I'd spent ten years, though, studying music with nuns during my New Zealand childhood, listening to their soft incantations and letting them slip holy pictures into my pocket for protection when I took music exams. I remembered them with great affection, those cloistered women who taught me to play music, and because of them I welcomed my occasional encounters with the nuns at St Mary's.

There were eight living units, awkwardly named after saints (the Anthonites, the Teresians, and so on), where an army of childcare workers took care of the children night and day, except for school hours. It was they who carried the main responsibility for the "milieu therapy"—establishing an environment in which every event from mealtimes to playtime was intended to be therapeutic. It was mostly the childcare staff, too, along with the teachers, who administered St Mary's watered-down behavior modification program, awarding points and rewards for good behavior, confiscating them for transgressions. Fortunately, in my view, it was understood that "B-mod" at St Mary's needed to be applied with discretion and flexibility, in conjunction with other more humanistic methods. Underlying all the various modalities was an ego-supportive approach intended to acknowledge and build on each child's strengths.

The psychologists presided over the living units and saw many of the children in individual therapy sessions, working with sand trays, punching bags, and puppets, sometimes taking kids outside to talk while they threw a ball or went for a walk. Once a week the whole department came together for a clinical seminar. I attended whenever I could, hungry to learn. I absorbed knowledge from whatever sources I could find, discussing my experiences with anyone who would talk to me, reading, writing up my sessions and pondering on what had happened and why. The children themselves taught me every day which of my ideas were productive and which were not. All of this, it turned out, was excellent preparation for the graduate program in music therapy that I entered a couple of years later.

I had come to the St Mary's Home for Children prepared not with formal training but with a lifelong involvement in the arts and a visceral personal knowledge of the healing that is to be found there. Music had been central in my life from my earliest days of singing with my sisters as toddlers and lying in bliss under the piano when our mother played for her own rare moments of escape into Bach or Beethoven. We all learned to play an instrument, taking lessons several times weekly throughout our childhood and playing together for fun as well as in concerts and competitions. We drew, painted, wrote poetry and stories. We acted out scenes from Shakespeare in the kitchen. We also lived in the shadow of violence and verbal attack—not on the scale of the abuse suffered by St Mary's children and countless others, but enough to have lasting effects. We turned our fear and helplessness on each other, with constant, hurtful fighting among the six of us.

For most of us, our creativity was our salvation, music most of all.

Singing in four-part harmony with my sisters, as we did often, was a potent counterforce to the strife that divided us. For me, playing my violin, painting, writing, gave me an arena and an outlet that allowed me to survive. I listened to music hungrily, both recorded and in concert, finding in it the realm of beauty, order, and hope that I so badly needed.

As a young adult I continued to make music. It was my great joy, my comfort, a way of expressing my often overwrought feelings, a way of connecting with others. I wrote, performed, and recorded songs, in spite of the sneering inner voices which had taken over from my now-distant family and told me persuasively that I was not good enough to be a musician. Improvising with others or alone was easier, once I became used to its freedom.

In my twenties I experienced another kind of healing through the arts when I joined with others to explore my husband Jonathan Fox's vision of a new kind of theatre, one that celebrated the true stories of ordinary people instead of fictional heroes and heroines. Together we developed a practice to embody this idea, an improvisational format in which members of our audiences told brief moments or whole episodes from their lives, then watched as we acted them out on the spot with dialogue, movement, and music. We named it Playback Theatre. After tentative beginnings in a church hall, we soon acquired confidence and a following. We learned how strong the hunger is to tell stories and to hear those of others. With roots in traditional storytelling and healing ceremonies, as well as in theatre practices like commedia dell'arte and in the therapeutic model of psychodrama, our theatre seemed to fill a modern void.

For me and for others in the group, the work was personally healing and a stimulus to growth. Drama games and exercises developed the flexibility and expressiveness of my body, my face, my words, my imagination. I rediscovered the delight of physical playfulness, lost to me as a small child. Listening to stories from real lives helped me to grow in understanding and compassion for others. I found a new sense of self-worth as I played back their stories and saw how much this creative reflection meant to the tellers. Sometimes I improvised music with the enactments, learning over time how to play spontaneously, matching the currents of emotion in the story. I stepped gingerly into the co-creative intimacy of the group and learned to trust it. When I grew brave enough to tell my own stories in rehearsal, I often gained new insight into my own life. Over and over again, I found acceptance and understanding from others. It changed me.

By the time I came to St Mary's, I had been immersed in Playback Theatre for almost ten years. I was formed by it, by its values, philosophy and practices, which I had also helped to establish. It was because of this that I began my work with the children with a profound respect for the particularity and subjectivity of the individual's story, knowing that it is through the stories that people tell of themselves that they comprehend their lives and build a sense of self.

Through both Playback and music I was committed to aesthetics, sensing that in artistic expression there is a redemptive framing of all human experience—"All suffering is bearable if it is seen as part of a story," says Isak Dinesen. Cautiously, experimentally, I developed my work at St Mary's based on what I knew—the primacy of story, the richness of music, and the promise of the arts as a way of growing, though it took a long time for me to feel the strength of my epistemology. I was at first far more uncomfortably aware of my lack of the kind of training that the other professionals had, the clinicians who worked with the children in play therapy, the recreation specialists, the medical staff who prescribed and monitored medication. I did not have the *Diagnostic and Statistical Manual* at my fingertips; I did not speak the lingo of treatment that I heard all around me. I was not well informed about the misery that many of the children came from: the stresses of poverty, both urban and rural, ill health, drug use, racism—stresses that can lead to abuse and neglect extreme enough to drive otherwise-normal children into madness.

But my naiveté was, looking back, not a bad way to enter this field. By the time I became a certified music therapist a few years later, I had discovered how valuable it was to meet the children first as fellow human beings, potential musicians, storytellers, and actors, looking at their charts only later when my own impressions could supplement the sad litany of dates and facts. My ignorance about clinical issues and methods of music therapy undoubtedly meant that I was not as effective in those first years as the children deserved. But I knew how to build a relationship; I knew what it meant to make music or act stories; I knew the power of imagination. I knew that the innate quality of meaning in art was related to a sense of meaning in life itself. This knowledge remained at the core of the approach I developed.

Two

A MUSICAL TORNADO

After I'd been at St Mary's for about a year I received a terse memo: the attic room in the cottage where I'd been seeing kids was to be partitioned into offices and would no longer be available for my sessions.

I had a week to find myself a new workspace.

"You're lucky you had the attic for as long as you did," said Patrick, the recreation director, who'd been at St Mary's for years. Patrick, an artist in his soul, was sympathetic with what I was trying to do with the music and drama program. "If you see anyplace around here that would work"—he gestured to the recreation area "you're welcome to use it."

The recreation department occupied a set of smallish, low-ceilinged rooms whose location in the basement reflected the place of recreation in the general hierarchy. Still, there were advantages, compared to the cottage. One was the ease of logistics—I'd only have to bring the kids downstairs, instead of struggling to keep them with me as we crossed the blacktop to the cottage. I wouldn't have to worry during the cold months about whether they'd remembered to bring a jacket with them to school. And although in the main building, the rec area was relatively secluded from the classrooms, living units, and therapy rooms.

One of the rooms, currently in a state of neglect, was the Space Room, so-called because of the psychedelic scenes of stars and rockets crudely painted on the windows, the legacy of an abandoned project. A trolley full of tattered books testified to someone's attempt to create a children's library. Broken toys and board games lay on a stained carpet. An old piano stood against the wall, out of tune and mistreated, although its tone was good and suggested a more dignified past. Some big pillows leaked stuffing onto the floor. The walls were covered with the same 70s vintage blue fabric; the innovation, I was told, of a staff member who had killed himself. No-one had wanted to remove his handiwork.

I saw the room's potential, though, and fate intervened on my behalf when the authorities decided that this part of the building was contaminated with asbestos and had to be overhauled. The soft-spoken czar of maintenance allowed me to pick out a new muted-red rug, design new secure closets, take down the sad fabric on the walls and paint them white. I scraped the black-painted space scenes off the windows and made gauzy cream-colored curtains to keep the children from being distracted from activity outside, and to prevent curious eyes from looking in. I mended the pillows and kept them to put in a circle or pile on one side of the room.

I moved in, establishing my territory with peremptory little signs on the wall: "Please leave this room tidy!" "Please supervise children using instruments." I was worried about my growing collection of drums and xylophones and other treasures. The Space Room was available to anyone else when I wasn't there, and I often came in to find the detritus of meals or games in my treasured domain.

The children liked the new Space Room. They would sink immediately onto one of the cushions, sighing with the release of tension as the door closed behind us. We heard other children going noisily by on their way to the gym or outside, shrieks from the swimming pool or the playground, sometimes the disturbing sounds of a child being restrained in the hallway. But the Space Room felt safe, separate, contained.

I had first worked with Rafael Rodriguez soon after I'd come to St Mary's. At that time he was a wiry and frenetic eight-year-old with moods that shot from delight to explosive rage and back within moments. A living embodiment of the fight-or-flight reflex, he might run from the room four or five times during a 40-minute session, unless he stayed to throw drumsticks or smash a chair to the floor. In the sunny times between rages he was a pleasure to be with, enthusiastic, adventurous and creative.

Rafael's story was a familiar one of trauma and deprivation, beginning before birth when his mother was beaten by his drug-addicted father. As an infant, Rafael was inconsolably distressed. His mother's hospitalization for mental illness made things worse. At three years old he lived on the streets of New York with his father for several months. Rafael's behavior as a small child was uncontrollable—fire-setting, insomnia, frightening temper tantrums. By the age of six he was suicidal. At seven he was admitted to a children's psychiatric hospital, then transferred a few months later to St Mary's. He saw his mother regularly, and she herself was doing well, but whether Rafael would ever be well enough to return to her care no one knew.

At eleven, Rafael was small and thin with neat features and big hazel eyes. He was still wildly energetic, still prone to running at the slightest frustration, still convinced that he was hopelessly incompetent. He was deeply mistrustful of almost everybody, adult or child. On the other hand, he loved music and had built a connection of sorts with me. The treatment team had recently recommended that he resume individual music therapy, hoping that it might help where other things had not. I agreed to the plan. I hoped that music could offer Rafael an opportunity to express his intense emotion in a creative way. I hoped, too, that music could be an arena for relationship. I knew from my own experience with him as well as from treatment reports that Rafael, like many other hurt children, tended to see other people as little more than suppliers or deniers of his own immediate demands.

The day came for Rafael's first session. He was happy to be doing music again. His oversized clothes flapped around skinny arms and legs as he flew from one activity to another with his habitual restlessness.

"Let's stay with the guitar a bit longer," I suggested, seeing him give up on a chord long before he'd had a chance to master it.

"Don't you tell me what to do!" he yelled, launching into a chaotic improvisation on the piano and drowning out his own words.

Listening to his wild and loud music, watching his desperate *same as Tim* agitation, I could sense the turmoil within him. I began to think of specific ways that music might be able to help, once I found the activities that engaged him for more than a minute. As well as giving him the chance to vent his feelings, I hoped that music's inherent organization in rhythm, harmony, and melody would soothe the anarchy inside him. Given Rafael's natural ability, music could also become an area in his life where he could be proud of his competence. If these goals were met, I'd expect to see some changes in his miniscule attention span.

diff

When I came to get him for his next session Rafael was in a foul mood. "He got into trouble in reading lab," his teacher whispered to me. Rafael leapt to his feet. "I want to go to music!" he shouted. "Do you think you can handle it?" Amy asked him. "Yes! Come on, Jo." He was already out the door. I threw a helpless look at Amy and ran after him. In the hallway he tried to hurt his hand in a door jamb, threatened to attack a boy returning from gym, threw himself down on the floor, then tore ahead of me to the Space Room where he sat scowling.

"Don't want to do *anything* ."

I went to the synthesizer and began a loud, discordant improvisation, trying to match his mood. Out of the corner of my eye I could see Rafael listening attentively. His body began to relax. "I want to play," he said after a couple of minutes. I made space for him beside me. He sat down, smiling.

"Show me how to play that tune!"

He was referring to a ragtime tune that I'd played last time. I began to teach him, one hand, one phrase at a time.

"No! I want to learn the whole thing!"

"This is how you learn it, one bit at time."

He could not accept it. He wanted to be able to play it now, this moment. The idea of investing effort for the sake of future satisfaction was entirely alien to his nature. He stood glowering. I kept playing the tune. His scowl gave way to a series of winks and twitches in time with the beat. Grinning at me, he danced like a puppet, exactly capturing the comical character of the music.

The following week Rafael walked in with an announcement. "I want to play the drums," He was referring to the recently-donated traps set in the closet. I hadn't yet learned how to set it up. "I know how to do it," he said confidently, but he didn't. Between us, with trial and error and a certain amount of impatience, we figured it out.

"You're going to help me put them away afterwards, right, Rafael?"

"Sure!"

Rafael was excited to find an instrument loud enough to match his own internal clamor. He managed to create more or less coherent patterns of sounds in spite of his unfamiliarity with the drums. But everything he played quickly collapsed in a vortex of escalated volume and speed. I tried to play the conga with him, to support his rhythm and steady the tempo.

"Stop!" he shouted. "I want to play by myself."

At last he tired of it, just when I was thinking that my ears could take no more. He jumped up from the stool, throwing the drumsticks on the floor, not angry this time but eager to move on to something else.

"I want to dress up and you play the drums for me and say who I am." Earlier in the day, in his impatience for his music session, Rafael had burst into the Space Room during a drama group. He'd seen the other kids dressing up and had been inspired.

Rafael rummaged through the box of assorted clothes, fabric pieces, and clown props.

"I'll be a priest," he said, holding up a long black piece of cloth and draping it around his shoulders. Then he spotted a gorilla mask. "No, I'll be King Kong." He put the mask on and made monster noises. "No! A wrestler!" He dropped the mask and swung around, taut and menacing. "Watch out because I can kill anyone!" By then the session was almost over. Amy would not be pleased if I brought a wrestler back to her classroom.

"Rafael, we have to end in a few minutes. It's time to put the drums away."

"No! Fuck you! I want to be Deadly Dave the wrestler!" He kicked the pile of costumes around the room. "I ain't gonna to help you do anything."

I started unscrewing bolts and collapsing stands. "Do you remember how you put the cymbal together?"

He studied it, suddenly absorbed in the problem. "Like this!" he said, dismantling it triumphantly. We put everything back in the closet. By the time we were walking back upstairs Rafael was feeling good. "I want to play the drums again next time, OK, Jo?" I shrank at the idea of submitting my ears to his drumming again. But within his frantic playing was the hint of musical order, something we could build on in the slow path toward healing the chaos in his soul. I knew this was a promise that music held for him: the purposefulness of rhythm and vibration as a reassurance against the frightening lessons that life had already taught him. "Sure," I said.

The next session Rafael stormed into the room, escorted by the crisis supervisor in whose custody he'd been since lunchtime.

"I want to play the synthesizer! By myself!"

It was clear that something had gone seriously wrong in his day— and that he'd been looking forward to his music session as an opportunity to express his distress. For twenty focused minutes he improvised first on the synth, then the conga drums, then the guitar. I sat and listened. He had the true musician's ability to find the music in any instrument, regardless of how little he knew its technique. The language of music, its inherent patterns of tone and rhythm, was Rafael's language. It spoke for him, giving him a voice for feelings too distant from words.

At one point, frustrated when he couldn't get the sound he wanted, he swung the guitar over his head.

"I'll smash the fucker!"

"*Rafael!*"

He put it down gently. "I wasn't really going to." He sat down again at the synthesizer and started playing. "This sounds like movie music," he said after a few minutes. "Like aliens. Let's make up a story."

Collaboratively, we invented a story in four scenes. Rafael created synthesizer sounds for each part of the story, experimenting until he was satisfied. I had never seen him so absorbed.

Rafael and I improvised our way through the music, pausing when it was time for him to set the synthesizer for the next phase. He was purposeful, his playing coherent and inventive. A jaunty little theme at the beginning of the story segued into ominous echoing bass sounds, followed by a screeching melisma in the upper register, and finally slow, broad chord clusters with the synthesizer's woodwind voice. "Let's practice one more time," he said when we finished. We went through it a couple more times, then taped it. "All *right!*" he said, delighted, when we played it back. "Let's act the story now." Cued by the "soundtrack" and directed by Rafael, I played the role of the aliens who are scary at first and then turn out to be harmless and lonely.

"Let's do it again!" said Rafael as the synth's final chords faded.

He wanted to do it several more times, thrilled with his creation.

It was time to leave, always a tense moment with Rafael.

"I want to have that tape," he said.

"The tape has to stay here, Rafael, because we're going to use it to record lots of things that you do."

"I want it for my own!" he shouted. His peaceful mood had vanished.

"You'd like to play it for the others upstairs, right?"

"*I want it!*" at the top of his voice.

"You could borrow it…" but Rafael had run from the room. I followed him as he disappeared around the corner and out into the playground. I summoned him sternly from the door. He scowled at me and ambled back, kicking stones.

"Hey, don't spoil it," I said as we walked toward his classroom. "That was wonderful, that music and the story."

"Yeah," he said, his scowl instantly replaced by a happy grin. "Sorry I ran outside, Jo. I was only pretending to be mad, you know."

I dropped into the nearest chair after bringing him back to Amy, wondering if his last-minute tantrum canceled out the earlier triumphs of the session.

It was like trying to stay astride a wild horse. Every session left me limp and out of breath. As the months passed I could see tiny increments in Rafael's self-control, in his retreat from the furthest reaches of rage. With the synthesizer or drums he was finding a musical voice for storms of emotion that would otherwise have driven him to violence or escape. There had been a number of times, like the session when he'd composed "movie" music, when the strength of his imagination and concentration had delighted both of us. I knew that, in his way, Rafael was growing fond of me and looked forward to our time together.

But his frustration and fury would return repeatedly, along threats to destroy something or run away. Sometimes I wondered if overall we were in fact making progress at all. The staff psychologist I saw for supervision advised me not to feel discouraged. "As long as a child wants to keep coming to therapy, you can assume that something beneficial is happening, whether it's obvious or not," he said. I kept going.

Rafael reached into his pocket when we got to the Space Room. "Here!" he said, handing me a granola bar. "It's for you. Saved it from snack." He announced in his peremptory way that he wanted to sing with the microphone. "Play with me while I sing."

I accompanied him on the guitar. Then, inspired by the microphone, he wanted to experiment. "I'm gonna make all kinds of sounds. Listen." He made a series of animal noises, then tried out voices for an old man, a tired girl, an angry boy. Pretending to be angry was enough to catapult him into his own ever-present fury. I tried to steer him back. "How about being a drunk old lady?"

"I don't want to be any old lady! Don't tell me what to do!" He rushed out into the hallway, but when I followed close on his heels he was standing beside the door, smiling at me and perfectly composed.

A few minutes later Rafael lost his temper again. "I'm really gonna run this time!" he yelled, leaping to his feet. But instead he dropped back into his chair. "What did you goddamn want to tell me anyway?"

By now this had happened a number of times—a flare-up immediately followed by Rafael's own re-assertion of composure. He was learning to step right through to the other side of his anger instead of being swept out to sea.

Next week Rafael was sitting in the living room of his unit when I came to pick him up.

"I'm waiting patiently for you," he said. He held up a small cardboard box. "This is my pet ant. I found him outside."

In the session he concentrated intensely on his playing and singing, sparkling with joy when he mastered the autoharp chords for "Yakety Yak" for the first time. He grabbed the little box and shook it open over the table. A confused ant dropped out.

"You watch, Jo. I've trained him. Now," he said to the ant, "dance while I play." He played the Yakety Yak accompaniment again, yelling instructions to the ant. The ant crawled one way and then another. "See!" screamed Rafael. "He's doing it!"

The ant safely back in its box, Rafael sat down at the drums and flew straight into one of his terrifyingly fast rhythms. It was like watching a brakeless car hurtle down a mountain road.

"This is a special thing that I wanted to show you," he yelled as he played.

I shouted back over the din, holding up my hand: "If you play a little slower you'll be able to do it much better."

"I don't want to play slower!" But a minute or two later he paused, then started again at a more manageable tempo. He grinned at me with delight when the rhythm spoke out clearly and steadily. It was an intricate pattern of three beats against four, something that few untrained players of any age would conceive of, let alone master.

We talked about all the different things he liked to do in music—singing, playing drums, and so on. Rafael had a suggestion. "How about if I do one thing for one week, then pick something else, like that."

For today's session he wanted to make up a rap song. He worked hard at it:

My name is Rafael and I am the best
Don't mess with me 'cause I'm so fresh
I can rap 'cause I'm not wack
So leave me alone and go back home

Rafael's voice rose in anger. His playing, however, remained strikingly controlled.

I'm tellin' you, babe, just stay away from me
You'd better get out
'Cause I'll kick your butt
Right to the ground

His tone softened into playfulness, syncopating the last lines:

So that's what I have to say
And that's the end of my rap, rap, rap

Rafael made up another about basketball. He was excited. "Let's tape it! And I want you to do it with me!" Rap with my New Zealand accent sounded peculiar, I thought, but Rafael didn't mind.

I'd found a practice pad for him so that he could drum without deafening himself and me. He enjoyed using it: "Hey, I'm like a real drummer in a band." He plunged into a wild volley of drumbeats, loud in spite of the practice pad's muted sound. I listened for a minute, then joined in on a hand drum, picking up the basic beat of his playing and holding it to a more or less regular tempo. As usual, his playing steadied in response: but this time, instead of keeping his head down, Rafael looked up at me, nodding his head in time to the beat. He locked eyes with me, smiling all the while.

We played for several minutes, the collaboration strong and creative. The music came to an end with a series of flourishes. Rafael reached over and held up a hand to slap me five. "That was cool!"

That session marked a turning point. We hadn't succeeded in the idea of one activity per session, but something more remarkable had happened. Rafael had discovered, at last, that playing in communication was more rewarding than the fiercely self-focused playing and singing he'd insisted on before. From that moment on, his preference was to play together. He was forging a musical and emotional connection with me, a link that would hold through the hard times that were in store for him.

The evening before the next session Rafael appeared at my desk during dinner time. He had remembered that on Monday nights I stayed late for the Anthonite singing group. "Hi, Jo, are you hungry?" He held out a plate with a slice of pizza and an apple. I gave him a hug, grateful and touched. He sauntered out. "See you tomorrow," he said, then leant back into the room, holding onto the door. "Don't be late!"

Rafael made up a little tune on the keyboard. He played it over and over again, experimenting with where it could go next and what shape he might bring to it. Remembering the opening phrase was difficult.

"We could write it down if you want," I offered.

"Shut up! I don't want to write it down." A minute later: "OK, write it down."

I took out some music paper and showed him how each line or space corresponded to a note on the keyboard. I wrote out the first notes of the tune, then played them, sight-reading the music.

"You mean that tells you what to play?" He was utterly intrigued.

I wrote out the rest of the tune. "Now we can remember it any time we want," I said, handing it to him. Rafael smiled proudly at the sheet of music.

"We should call it something." He thought for a minute. "How about 'Strange Rodriguez?'" He wrote it on the top of the page and we went upstairs to make a copy for Henry, a musician on the childcare staff and Rafael's musical role model.

Rafael felt a kinship, not always harmonious, with all the amateur musicians on the staff. One day he came in fuming about something that had happened in the group. It seemed that Mario, one of the younger childcare workers, had insulted him in some way. He brushed off my questions. "I want to rap!" His rap was about rapping itself. I accompanied him on the conga, supporting the passion of his spontaneous lines. The cause of his anger became apparent as he went on: Mario, I gathered, had made claims of being an expert rapper and had been recognized as such by others in the Jeromists, boys and staff. Rafael, his precarious pride invested in his own talent as a rapper, was furious, but his fury was aimed mostly at himself. His voice rose in a fierce crescendo: "I'm a jerk! Jerk! Jerk! Jerk!"

A week later Rafael was in a singing mood and chose the calypso song "Day-O." I harmonized with him, a rare pleasure for me. Although many of the St Mary's children were musically gifted and sang well in tune, they were far less able to maintain a tune against another part, even in a simple round, than ordinary children of similar age and musicality. I could only speculate that the ability to hold a harmony part was a function of ego strength as much as musicality. Rafael was an exception to this tendency, and he enjoyed singing in harmony as much as I did. "Teach me what you just sang." Concentrating, he picked it up with ease. "OK, now you sing the tune and I'll do the other one." We sang it again in two parts, Rafael singing harmony this time. He was enchanted by the effect. "Let's tape it so I can play it for Mario. He loves this song."

It was clear that he was thinking of Mario as a fellow-musician, not a competitor.

I gave a case presentation on Rafael for the St Mary's clinical staff. I told them some of the story of our work together, how I had hoped from the beginning that Rafael's natural affinity with music would eventually allow the inherent orderliness of music to mitigate the wild anarchy within him; how he'd begun to use music not just for the one-sided discharge of emotion but as an arena for relationship. Some of the psychologists listened with interest, others nodded distantly. A couple of them, including Jason, Rafael's clinical coordinator, sat at the table catching up on their paperwork, to my annoyance. Jason had made it clear often enough that he did not think highly of music therapy.

Then I played them a tape of some of Rafael's music. The clinicians sat up, startled and wincing at the distorted volume of Rafael's drumming. The first few cuts sounded like the manic boy they all knew—the furious snare drum, the fraught voice yelling semi-coherently over it. The music began to change. The machine-gun drumming, desperate though it was, hinted at order and purpose within its chaos. In several excerpts the fortissimo playing built in intensity and then spent itself, giving way to subtlety and playfulness. There were moments of what could only be called tenderness. The therapists could hear how his music found connection with mine, linking with the support and structure of the conga or keyboard. Jason put away his notes and looked at me thoughtfully as a musical dialogue unfolded between Rafael and myself in an ever-more inventive call-and-response. The final improvisation traveled a musical journey from turbulent intensity to a long keyboard dénouement of almost meditative quality. "That's *Rafael*?" asked the clinical director. I knew they were hearing a side of him that was usually invisible and unsuspected. It felt important to me that the other staff members knew there was more to Rafael than his manic wildness.

Shortly after this time Rafael began to slide toward a crisis. He and his family had been meeting once a month with a social worker to discuss his permanent return home within the next year. Rafael had often talked about the day he'd live with his mother again, but as the time approached he panicked. There were worried reports about a relapse into violence and running away. Rafael began muttering about suicide and was placed on constant supervision. Discharge plans were postponed indefinitely. He kept coming regularly to music sessions, anxious and troubled but holding firmly onto his connection to the music and to me.

"I could see him more than once a week for a while, if he'd want to," I suggested tentatively to Jason, remembering his skeptical attitude when I'd made a similar suggestion with another child.

"That'd be great," said Jason, not hesitating. "Let's do it. I'll talk to him today."

For several weeks Rafael would burst into the Space Room like a suffocating person finding open air. He played for dear life, holding fast to the familiar tunes and instruments, to the pattern we'd established of wordless musical dialogue followed by an easing of tension and an opening into expansive creativity.

Eventually his desperation about leaving grew less. His behavior in class and in the group subsided to its usual eccentric character. No-one mentioned discharge: the plan was to wait a few months before bringing it up again.

"Rafael, now that you're doing so much better, do you want to go back to having music once a week instead of twice?" I asked him as we were putting the synthesizer away one day.

He didn't look up but answered firmly. "Nope, I want to keep coming like this." It was fine with me.

Rafael came for a session a few days after his first visit home following his crisis. He ambled out of his classroom, looking grumpy and unkempt, then flashed me his sunbeam smile. During the short walk to the music room, he jumped down a flight of stairs, swung from a pipe, leaped up to touch a light fixture. In the Space Room he set up the snare drum, the bass drum and the cymbal—the three loudest instruments. Listening to the rhythm he was trying to establish, I played a pulse on the conga to support it. His playing immediately acknowledged mine, but he quickly interrupted himself.

"Wait! I'm trying to play something I heard in the subway." In between volleys of drumbeats, he told me about a band he and his mother had heard in a subway station.

"How was it, being at home this time?" I said, wanting him to feel free to talk more if he wanted to.

"I don't want your damn questions!"

It was hard for Rafael to recreate the rhythm he heard in his imagination. Frustrated as he was, though, he put his anger into his music instead of running or throwing things. We continued playing.

"You made me screw up!" he yelled. I stopped.

Rafael tried again and screwed up all by himself. He threw his arms up in the air in exasperation. "Shit! *Damn!*"

"I'll just sit and listen," I said. "You can tell me if you want me to play."

His tension broke up like ice on a spring river. "You can play," he said, gesturing to the conga and small percussion I had beside me.

As we played, in collaboration again, Rafael called out the story: "All these people were walking by and getting on the train, but me and my mom just wanted to listen. We stayed there for an hour, just her and me, nobody else was there." He meant no one else from his contentious family.

Suddenly, the music fell into a groove. I didn't know if it was exactly the rhythm that Rafael was seeking but it had its own complex integrity, our own blending of timbres and patterns. Rafael gazed at me as he played. When we paused after some minutes, Rafael sighed.

"That was *good*," he said happily. "I should play this in a band!"

"One day you'll have your own band and I'll come and listen."

"You won't come and listen," he said laughing, "you'll come and *play*."

I'd begun teaching Rafael how to relax. He was always physically wound up like a spring, ready to hurtle across the room. We often now began sessions with a few minutes of yoga-style relaxation and breathing. Rafael enjoyed these moments of peace. One day in April he came in flushed and excited from a baseball game on the big field. It was his last session with me before an extended home visit, a trial run for his permanent departure in June. He dropped onto the big pillow and closed his eyes. "OK, play that music." He meant a recording of meditative piano music that we'd been listening to, more varied and aesthetic than most "relaxation" music.

It took Rafael longer than usual to unwind. The first piece came to an end just as he at last took a deep breath. Without opening his eyes he said "Don't turn it off."

The music changed to a slow blues. He sat up, still calm, and began to improvise a song. It was about wandering in open spaces, rather poetic and vague. The melody he sang was perfectly attuned to the harmonies of the music.

The blues piece ended and the next one began, a gospel-flavored theme this time. Rafael sang about Martin Luther King.

Again the music changed, this time to contemplative modal chords. Rafael sank onto the floor and nestled beside the piano, still singing. His words became more personal.

"You gave me love for a long, long time. You knew what I needed when I couldn't say. I still need you day by day. Please stay with me, please stay."

He sang for several minutes. When the tape ended he didn't move. Holding my breath, not wanting to break the spell, I stepped to the piano and continued playing in the same vein as the recording, as best I could with my limited keyboard skill. Rafael kept singing, his eyes closed again. His voice was full and heartfelt, musically related to the pianissimo chords I was playing.

"You are the one who listened, when all I did was yell." Rafael had never expressed himself like this before. I could hardly believe, until he made it explicit, that he was addressing me. "I'll see you after Easter, and we'll do music again," he sang.

At last Rafael paused. He had been singing for close to an hour. He stood up, smiling, and hugged me. We were both silent.

"Have a great time at home, Rafael," I said at last. There seemed no way to comment on the extraordinary thing that had just happened.

He hugged me again when we got back to his unit. "See you soon, Jo."

At the end of the day I found Jason in his office. "Do you have a minute?" I said. "I'd like to tell you about what happened with Rafael today." It sounded unlikely even to me as I described it—Rafael, so articulate and self-aware, so openly expressing love and need, so unwaveringly focused for an hour, so subtle in his music? Yet it had happened. I felt awe at this glimpse of a soul usually walled from view.

Jason listened with scant interest. "I'm glad he's doing well."

Once again Rafael's family and the social worker were meeting to plan his discharge at the end of the spring semester. He was already thirteen, the upper age limit for children at St Mary's. This time he was ready. He and his mother were full of plans for the summer and then his return to public school in the fall. I was happy to see him looking forward to his new life but I knew I'd miss him. I had known Rafael for five years.

Rafael's mother came up from the city for Awards Day, a highlight of the year when every child received an award from the school for achievements ranging from academic prowess to "Most Cheerful" in the classroom. Emotions always ran high on Awards Day; anxieties about the awards themselves, tensions about leaving, disappointments about not leaving, the presence of parents and siblings often as volatile as the St Mary's kids themselves. Still, it was a festive and happy time. The staff allowed themselves to revel for once in the love that virtually all of them felt for the children.

The ceremony was held on the playground. As the last awards were being distributed, the wind rose and the sky darkened to a sickly gray-yellow. Someone came running outside. "There's a tornado warning! Everyone inside immediately!" The staff spun into efficient bossiness, herding children and families toward the building. I was standing with Rafael and his mother, whom we'd invited to visit the Space Room. "Let's go," I said. Rafael clutched his award for "Most Improved Attention Span" to his chest as we ran up the steps. We got inside just as huge drops of rain began to fall.

Ms Rodriguez was a pretty woman with smooth dark hair and an unsure air about her. She looked like a rounder, calmer version of Rafael. "Rafael's told me all about his music here," she said, surveying the Space Room. We pulled chairs close together. Thunderstorms were common but a tornado was different, unpredictable and frightening. The lights went out, leaving us in soft semi-dark.

Rafael's favorite instruments were set up in readiness, though the synthesizer was useless without electricity. He sang his songs and played drums with the control and musicality that by then he'd mastered. His mother listened entranced.

"I didn't know you could play like that!" she said when he paused. "You'll have to keep playing when you're home."

"Nothing can stop me!" said Rafael.

"Rafael, can I show you something too?" said Ms Rodriguez, hesitantly. "I write poems sometimes — did you know that?" Outside, rain was falling in cascades but the sky had retreated to ordinary-looking storm clouds split now and then with lightning. Rafael's mother recited her poem, about finding hope when things are hard.

"Wow, Mom!" Rafael was impressed. "Say another one."

For another twenty minutes they exchanged songs and poems, sometimes singing together, until we all jumped at a loud knock on the door. I opened it to find an exasperated Pauline, the supervisor from Rafael's group. "We had no idea where you were! We've been worried. Rafael's mom has to get on the bus right now."

In the tornado panic Pauline had forgotten that I'd arranged to bring Rafael and his mother to the Space Room after the awards ceremony. I was apologetic about keeping them so long, but I didn't regret the chance that Rafael and his mother had had to experience each other's art.

A few weeks later Rafael came for his final session, keyed up about leaving St Mary's the next day. He wanted to play as much as he could in the time we had. In spite of his excitement his music was still organized, still creative and connected. I gave him a tape with a collection of favorite songs from our years together.

It was time to end. Rafael was shy. "We'll always remember each other, I think," I said.

"Yeah!"

"Maybe you'll came back and visit some time."

"If I do I'll play music with you."

"Goodbye, Rafael." I held him for a moment.

"Bye, Jo," he said into my shoulder.

Three

LIZZIE THE MERMAID

I'd met Lizzie on my first day as an employee of St Mary's and began working with her some months later. She stands out for me as one of the most remarkable and most tragic of all the children I came to know, in the horror of her story, the depth of her illness, and the triumphant flowering of her music.

On that first day Dr Fisher had sent me down to the playground to observe some of the kids I'd be working with. A watery March sun shone low in the sky. Staff members huddled in down parkas while children played ball, whizzed around on small bicycles, jumped rope or played on the swings. I sat down on the stone wall near Marilyn, a senior childcare worker whom I'd met that morning.

I watched as Marilyn expertly handled the constant small conflicts that sparked like brushfires.

"Lizzie Jimenez!" she yelled as one child's voice rose in obscenities directed at another. "Time out! Now!"

Lizzie spat out one final curse and wheeled away from her adversary, a stocky boy shorter than herself. She was about nine years old, slender and pretty with a tangle of dark hair. She moved with abrupt jerky movements like a marionette. She sat down close to Marilyn, slumped over folded arms and muttering under her breath. After a while she noticed me. Her expression changed to curiosity.

"Who are you?" she said.

"My name's Jo," I said, pleased at this friendly approach.

"That's a boy's name."

"Well, I'm not a boy."

"What's your real name?"

"Josephine."

She tried it out, grinning. "Josephine."

"And you're Lizzie?"

Lizzie scowled. "I'm an asshole." She jumped up and stood in front me. "So cute," she crooned, stroking my hair. She kissed me on the cheek, then climbed onto my lap. Her body was lightweight and tense. I put my arms around her.

Marilyn looked over at us. "Lizzie!" She sounded reproving.

"I don't mind," I said.

"She doesn't know you, it's not appropriate," she explained to me as Lizzie clambered down from my lap. "Appropriateness," as I soon learned, was a much-used criterion of acceptable behavior.

Lizzie, who'd been at St Mary's for about a year, had been in play therapy for a while and had developed a strong relationship with her therapist. But she did not seem to be improving. The treatment team thought that music might at least give her an opportunity to vent her always-turbulent feelings in a different way, and perhaps help her to develop a more positive sense of herself. Lizzie herself was eager to try music, though whether it was music itself, or me, or just the chance of additional attention that attracted her we didn't know at first. It didn't matter: as I repeatedly discovered with other children, the eagerness to do music was essential for the therapy to be effective.

Some time after our meeting that first day I'd learned Lizzie's story. Her mother had committed suicide when she was a baby and she had been placed in foster care. Each weekend, her father took her for visits during which he would tie her to a bed and rape her repeatedly. In her three-year-old way she tried to tell her foster family, but they didn't believe her until she was diagnosed with a venereal disease. By then she was unmanageably disturbed and had been in institutions ever since. Like most severely abused children, Lizzie was convinced that she was a hopelessly bad person, proven—as she herself would say— by her constant fights with other kids. In school she was often disruptive and had trouble learning basic academics, although she was articulate and intelligent. In team meetings there were often amused and somewhat exasperated reports of Lizzie's latest claim to identity. She was intensely interested in exploring who she was, and to some degree the alternate names and self-descriptions she asserted so vehemently were probably unconscious attempts to insist on an alternative story to the tragedy that her own life had forced onto her.

I would have worked with Lizzie somewhat differently if I had met her in my later years at St Mary's. With more knowledge and experience, I might have tried Playback Theatre techniques, for instance, to help Lizzie tell her core story, a necessary step in healing from trauma — although some victims, and Lizzie might have been one, have been too dreadfully hurt to be healed even by truth-telling. I would probably have encouraged her to compose her own songs. As it was, our work consisted mostly of Lizzie's choosing, learning, and singing folk songs, through which she expressed her intense feelings and gave rein to a talent which she had never before discovered. Our time together — weekly sessions for a period of two and a half years — was also an arena for a strong connection between us, meaningful, I think, to her as well as to me.

Lizzie and I walked across the playground to the cottage with its attic room which I was still using at that point. Older, more stable children lived here: Lizzie's own unit, the Anthonites, composed of the youngest and most disturbed boys and girls, was housed in the main building. It was our fourth session together. So far we'd spent our 45 minutes in a combination of drama games and singing. I was taking my cue minute by minute from Lizzie's interests and responses with the general intention of giving her the chance as much as possible to express her feelings and to find reasons to be pleased with herself. In her classroom and group life, Lizzie was well aware of being a notorious failure.

The cottage was empty and the attic quiet, a relief after the pandemonium of the main building. My collection of simple percussion instruments and flutes stood invitingly on display in one corner. In another corner was a suitcase overflowing with pieces of fabric for dressing up and drama games. Lizzie swathed her head in a piece of gold cloth, her first move each session. It seemed to mark something for her, perhaps reminding her of the private, creative self she returned to each music session.

"Lizzie, let's sing." In our sessions so far I'd discovered that this girl had an extraordinary soprano voice, soaring and true. No one, least of all Lizzie, seemed to have known this about her. Her preference was for plaintive folk songs, which she learned readily. I showed her a new one:

How it breaks my heart to leave you
Now the carnival is gone

"Do you like it?" I asked her after I sang it.
She had tears in her eyes. "I want to learn it but it makes me cry." Lizzie often had strongly emotional responses to the songs that I showed her. Whether it was the lyrics or the poignancy of the music itself that moved her, it was evident that singing tapped into her deep well of sadness and yearning. Certainly she herself sought and welcomed the experience of being moved.

The next session Lizzie requested "The Carnival is Over" and sang it with me, remembering the lyrics from last week. We sang it four times in a row at her insistence. Each time her eyes filled when we got to the last verse:

High above, the dawn is breaking
This will be our last goodbye....

"Josephine! Write out the words for me, please." I wrote them for her. She hid the piece of paper under her T-shirt, a secret treasure to take back to her room.

A week later Lizzie found me in the hallway talking to Dr Fisher. She inserted herself between us, hugging me tightly and reaching up to hit my nose. "Josephine! It's time!" In the music room we began to learn a new song, a children's song about bossy grownups and wriggly kids. She found the song funny and collapsed into giggles verging on hysteria, crawling around on hands and knees and snuffling through her nose like a baby animal. She was stimulating herself more with every step. "Something's feeling my vagina," she said, and insisted I come with her to the bathroom to look. All I saw were her little light-brown private parts, thin and innocent.

"If I sing the Carnival song it'll calm me down," she said, and it did. But her mood came back when it was time to leave. She insulted me all the way up to the main building.

Lizzie's hysterical giggles often reappeared, as did her "baby animal" character. Often she'd fly into anger at me for an unpredictable variety of sins—singing with her, or failing to sing with her; reminding her that it was time to end; praising her too warmly. But the anger would abruptly disappear and she'd climb on my lap with remorseful kisses. Lizzie's volatility and craziness perplexed me. I was sure only of two things, her musical affinity and the connection that had grown between us.

Towards winter we began to sing Christmas songs. She loved the old carols.

"Josephine," she said one day, interrupting "The First Noel," "I love you. When I'm asleep I hear you in my dream." She paused. "I'm scared you're going to leave."

"I'm not planning to leave, Lizzie. I like it here."

"Josephine, I think you're going to leave because of me, because I'm a fuckhead." I tried to convince her that she was in fact one of the reasons I liked my work so much. Lizzie often talked about what a terrible person she was. There was a paradoxical power in the conviction that what had happened to her was her fault: if she had made it happen by being bad, then perhaps she could prevent it happening again if she learned how to be good.

Eventually she turned her attention to questions prompted by the Christmas songs—was Jesus born through his mother's vagina? Did he drink milk from her breasts? At the end of the session she became hysterical again, lying on the floor and giggling. I was learning to read her a bit better.

"Lizzie, are you doing this because you want to stay here with me?"

She sat up, solemn again. "Yes." She thought about it for a minute, then got to her feet and left with me calmly.

Lizzie got angry with me again the next session when I insisted that she put away the flute and a drumstick after she'd threatened to hit me with them. "I'll never come here with you again!" Then suddenly contrite—"I know you'll leave, because I'm so bad." "No, Lizzie, you're not bad, and I'm not leaving."

She worked hard on learning "The First Noel." She sang it

beautifully, her voice rising effortlessly to the high notes. "I want to sing it for the whole school!" she said. She'd never before indicated pride in her singing. She decided she'd like first to sing it for Trip, her favorite childcare worker. I was pleased to hear her talking about sharing her singing. It would certainly be a milestone if she could sing for others with anything like the confidence and pleasure she was by now showing in her sessions.

At the end she talked again about her fear that I might leave. "But not because of me, right, Josephine?" When we got back to her group she sang "The First Noel" for Trip. She was shy but composed. "Beautiful, Lizzie," he praised. He was surprised. I'd been telling the treatment team about Lizzie's progress, but until now no one had seen her unusual ability for themselves.

After Christmas Lizzie came in with some news.

"Josephine, I'm turning into a boy," she told me as soon as we were alone. She made me lean down so she could whisper. "I'm turning into Johnny O'Keeffe." Johnny O'Keeffe was a boy in her living unit. We talked for a while about why she might prefer to be Johnny O'Keeffe. Her reasons, it emerged, were principally that she would not have to have sex with boys if she were a boy herself, and secondly that she'd have more control, in general, over what happened to her once she grew up.

I agreed with her about the advantages of being a boy. "But girls can also decide what happens to them or who they have sex with," I said. It was a new and not very convincing idea for Lizzie.

Next time I saw her she was hostile and angry toward me. "I don't want to listen! I don't want to play!" Eventually I began to play some music by myself, improvising on the frame drum and resonator bells. The music was slow but rhythmic. "That is dumb music!" she sneered. But in a moment she forgot her anger and joined in with a wood block, punctuating the rhythm with her usual sensitivity and subtlety. After a few minutes she paused.

"You see, I do hate Lizzie," she said earnestly. "She's sort of OK but I still hate her. She needs to get more love and care than she does here and that's why she has to be sent away."

Children in severe crisis were occasionally sent to a psychiatric hospital for a period of further treatment. I wondered if someone had been telling her that she might have to go. I'd never heard Lizzie talking in the third person about herself like that.

"Well, I like Lizzie. I like her very much," I said. "She has a loving heart, and she's very intelligent, and she's an incredible singer."

"She's a dork," said Lizzie.

"Some really sad things have happened to her, and she's trying hard to cope with them."

Lizzie stared at me. "I feel sorry for her too."

I thought it might be time to challenge her gently. "She's really you, isn't she, Lizzie?"

"No! No! I'm Johnny O'Keeffe!"

I didn't contradict her. She held tightly to my arm all the way back to the group.

"I want to tell you something," she said next time we got together. "I'm an Apache Indian. Did you know that?" Apparently Johnny O'Keeffe had been forgotten.

"No, I didn't know that. I thought you were Puerto Rican."

"Well, I might be a Mexican, really." She was eager to learn a Mexican song that I knew. At the end of the session I played her a tape of the guitarist Christopher Parkening playing, as she correctly identified, music from Spain. Lizzie was constantly surprising me by her general knowledge, often idiosyncratically applied.

For several weeks she talked very seriously about being an Apache Indian. "My name is *Red Fox Pacho*," she said, hissing the name in my ear. She learned "Cielito Lindo," singing it with gusto and accompanying herself with drumsticks on the floor in a bouncing rhythm.

"Josephine, my hair is black because I'm Indian, did you know that?" A week later she said: "I'm really an Asian Indian, not Apache, Josephine."

Although it was obviously a sign of her disturbance, there was also a strong thread of creativity in this dedicated exploration of identity: why not invent herself anew when her original self had been so violated? I wasn't sure that it was either wise or possible to bring her back to a more conventional sense of reality. Instead I accepted her as she presented herself to me, constantly offering her the world of music where melody, harmony, and rhythm made their own unassailable sense. If I knew any music from the culture she was currently identifying with, I'd offer to play it or teach it to her.

Lizzie's unfailing eagerness to sing, to learn new songs, to improvise together, told me that music was indeed a place where she was finding something that she needed—an arena of creativity and connection that allowed her to transcend the narrowness forced on her by trauma. Lizzie's singing voice, unfettered and pure, spoke of this girl's innate humanity. The pioneering music therapy team of Nordoff and Robbins wrote of the "Music Child," meaning the healthy, creative core personality of an otherwise-impaired child who finds a degree of expression and fulfillment in music which may not be accessible any other way. Lizzie, who saw herself and was seen by almost everyone in her world as damaged and hopeless, became the Music Child in the safe, intimate, and creative atmosphere of our sessions.

The day after her eleventh birthday Lizzie seemed sad and withdrawn. She stood at the window, beating on it with a pair of mallets, then hitting herself on the head. I stopped her. She went back to her rhythm on the window. I tried to play with her, but she froze, resuming only when I stopped. After a while I sang "The Carnival" very softly. She accompanied me with the sparsest of beaten rhythms, her face still. I began another song about love. Lizzie crept into my lap. She sighed deeply several times and fell asleep.

After a break at the beginning of the summer, Lizzie came back to music sessions with a new identity to report to me.

"Josephine, I have to tell you, I'm really Hawaiian. Well, actually I'm a Hawaiian *mermaid*. Don't tell anyone else."

We played music on the bells and percussion for most of the session, a rather ethereal dialogue that became increasingly energetic and adventurous. Lizzie made up a little four-note theme and played it again as we ended, looking up at me with a grin.

"That was real mermaid music," she said, satisfied.

A week later her mood was grim. "I'm a retard!" she said angrily. "I'm a self-abuser!" Her childcare staff had warned me about repeated crises in the living unit. "Josephine, Trip is going to leave, did you know that?"

I knew that he was changing jobs within the institution, moving from childcare to recreation. There had been some concern about how Lizzie would take his departure. Trip had expressed some relief about being out of her reach in his new position. I reminded her that she'd still see him when she went to recreation.

"Josephine, I love him too much." She was convinced, of course, that she'd driven him away. "Can you sing a song about goodbye, Josephine?"

I sang "Four Strong Winds:"

Our good times are all gone, and I'm bound for moving on
I'll look for you if I'm ever back this way

Lizzie listened, not singing, tears standing in her wide brown eyes.

As we walked back she talked about Hawaii and mermaids again. "Is Hawaii in the Pacific? And New Zealand too?" I had told her about New Zealand earlier, and how I'd grown up there before coming to the States. She had been intrigued to hear about the brown-skinned New Zealanders, the Maori.

"Josephine." Her tone was desperately serious. "When you go to New Zealand, would you please find a family for me?"

The next session, in rapid succession:

"I'm an angel."

"I'm a mermaid."

"I'm Puerto Rican" (the first time she'd ever said this).

"I'm all Polynesian but I'm half Puerto Rican too."

She wanted me to teach her a song in Maori, since it was a Polynesian language. She was quick to pick up the unfamiliar syllables, fitting them into the lilting tune with ease.

Strolling by the stream near the cottage a couple of weeks later, Lizzie said she remembered the "Polynesian" song, "Po Kare Kare," and sang the first verse without prompting. "Now can we sing the Carnival song, because it's Trip's last day?" We began the song, but she soon fell silent, contorting her face into her "baby animal" character and pushing my head as I sang.

"Josephine! Did I tell you that I'm really a *leprechaun* mermaid?"

The next session Lizzie sang "Po Kare Kare," beginning spontaneously on the correct note. I wondered, not for the first time, if she had perfect pitch, a rare gift even among musicians.

"Lizzie Jimenez, you're wonderful!" I said. She was flustered and scolded me for saying her name like that. She talked again about longing to be a mermaid. I began to make up a song about wishing. She interrupted me.

"Sing that you wish you were a mermaid too."

"But I don't want to be a mermaid, I'd rather be a person." She turned away from me. I knew she had good reason for wanting to be a mermaid, safely undivided below the waist.

After the session we walked to the playing field to join her group.

"The thing is, I'm going to make a movie about a mermaid in seven years' time," she said as we crossed the bridge over the stream. "But you'll be too old to be in it. You might even die by then."

"I'll be older but I probably won't be dead."

"I don't want you to die. I don't want you to be old." She grabbed my hand and kissed it, squeaking and snuffling like an animal. "That means 'I love you'," she translated for me. She repeated it several times.

When I came to the group to pick up another child Lizzie drew me aside urgently. She had a length of fabric and insisted that I show her how to wear it like a sari. She'd apparently obtained it from the sewing room by telling Dolores, the seamstress, that I'd said she must have it. I scolded her gently for misrepresenting me to Dolores. She was furious, then twisted her wrists hard, trying to hurt herself. I reached for her hands. She hugged me fiercely.

I talked to Dolores who didn't mind giving Lizzie the fabric. It was too short for a sari, so I tied it on her dhoti-style. She modeled it for the Anthonite group, delighted by their admiration. Inspired, she looked over at me. "Can we sing 'Po Kare'?" The other kids listened appreciatively. Lizzie sighed with deep satisfaction. She'd never before taken the risk of singing solo in front of the other children.

We met again after a couple of weeks off between summer session and the beginning of school. "Josephine! I think you probably won't die soon because actually you look quite young."

We talked about Navajos, archaeology, death and posterity. As we were leaving she said: "You know what the best thing about being a girl is?"

"What?" I was glad to hear that she was at last finding advantages in being a girl.

Lizzie leaned forward intently. "You can grow your hair as long as you friggin' want."

Her mood was becoming more and more volatile. She was angry at me for most of the next session, for calling her Lizzie instead of Elizabeth; for not giving her the small keyboard quickly enough when she demanded it; for expressing uncertainty about her being a Navajo; for refusing to tell Marilyn about an imaginary bump on her head. She had developed a habit of asking me to report physical problems to her staff. I wanted her to tell them herself.

At the treatment team meeting some of the other staff members expressed concern, feeling that Lizzie was losing ground. They talked about increasingly frequent outbursts where she would try to hurt herself, and the dogged insistence on one delusion or another. With me, her mood continued to veer between calmness, affection, and hostile rage. The flow of her creativity remained constant. She loved to sing the songs she knew, to learn new ones, to improvise with instruments. Singing or playing, she would grin in delight.

I showed Lizzie a new song from a book I'd found called "Songs for Self-esteem," which in spite of its clinical-sounding title seemed up to her aesthetic standards:

Shine like the morning star
Spreading light from near to far
Feeling proud of who you are
Shine like a star

She devoted herself to learning it with her usual artistic seriousness. At her request I taught her a harmony part, which she learned and sang with ease.

"I wish," she said, pausing as we sang together, "that I had your voice."

"I'd be quite happy to have yours," I said. She was surprised but accepted this reciprocal tribute.

This was the day that I had to tell her that in a few weeks I was going away to New Zealand for several months on a long-awaited visit to my family. I myself felt torn about going, knowing what it would mean to the children I worked with, especially Lizzie. She froze, her face blank.

"I'm going to live in Trip's house when I'm thirteen," she said at last. "You can bring me a wig from Hawaii. I could be a mermaid in the Pacific. There are lots of mermaids in the Pacific, but no sharks."

When we went back to the group she lost control, attacking the childcare worker, the other children, and finally me. We held her firmly until she calmed down. I stayed with her for a long time.

In our last session before I left, Lizzie talked with intensity about turning into an angel. "That way I can go wherever I want, I could go to Trip's house if I wanted." She wanted a new name, Dorian, for her angel self.

I told her that two staff members had said they'd be glad to sing with her while I was away, though in fact I wasn't confident that they'd find the time. I promised her I'd be back.

But Lizzie wasn't there when I returned. They told me that her deterioration had continued to the point where she had had to be sent to a children's psychiatric hospital. No one knew if she'd improve enough to come back. She was by then almost thirteen, the age when children are discharged from St Mary's.

I visited Lizzie in the hospital, an hour and a half away. She had grown taller, less child-like, still slender and strikingly beautiful. She took my reappearance calmly, as though she knew I would come sooner or later. She was quiet, resigned; probably sedated. We sang together. She remembered the Carnival song and "Shine Like a Star." She said there was no music at the hospital.

"When am I going to come back, Josephine?"

"Soon, I hope, Lizzie." I gave her a large iridescent shell from the beach in New Zealand.

She did come back, but only briefly before being permanently discharged to a state hospital in New York City. I sent her notes and messages until I could visit, a few months later, finding my way with some anxiety through a run-down and unfamiliar part of the city. The brick hospital buildings blocked the sky. Doors swung and locked. I waited in a dingy visiting room and eventually Lizzie was brought to me. She was clearly far worse. Between the adolescent changes in her mind and body, the stresses of this new environment, and the inexorable unfolding of the consequences of her father's brutality, Lizzie had crossed a line into a place where I couldn't reach her, at least not in this short visit. She knew who I was, of course, but the mutuality of our connection was gone. She didn't want to sing. She had a new obsession, a popular movie actor whom she was sure was going to adopt her. She talked about him, giggling and barely coherent, plucking compulsively at the skin on her arm, until the attendant came to take her away for dinner.

I spent half an hour with the psychologist who was monitoring Lizzie's treatment. He seemed a good-hearted man, compassionate and concerned about her. He had seen Lizzie go downhill in the months since her admission and shook his head over the question of her future. He was open and respectful to me but a little puzzled as to who I was in relation to Lizzie. I did not know myself whether I still had any role in her life.

I never saw Lizzie again. I continued to send her notes and occasional little gifts but with no sign or conviction that it meant anything to her. After a while I stopped.

During my time with Lizzie, and since, I've wondered what did the music we did together meant to her. It certainly was not a "cure." Lizzie had been driven into possibly permanent madness by the events of her early childhood. Her varying identities, her violent mood swings, her inclination to hurt herself, her obsessions were all signs of serious mental illness. And yet this fragmented and suffering child had at her core a musicality that was the essence of health and creativity—the "Music Child." Judith Herman in *Trauma and Recovery* comments about the abused child's imperative "to preserve hope and meaning." For Lizzie, the chance to use her beautiful voice and her aesthetic awareness to make music gave her a sustained experience of a place where order and beauty prevailed: the realm of music itself. Every session became an opportunity to express the intensity of her feelings through songs and instrumental music. She also built and maintained a loving relationship with me. Lizzie's humanity, so tragically occluded in her early life, was revealed again in this arena of connection and artistic expression.

Four

SINGING WITH THE ANTHONITES

I talked to Marilyn about setting up a regular singing session with the children in the Anthonites. I was seeing several of them in individual sessions and didn't have time to see more. But every time I came to the group to pick up Lizzie or one of the others, I'd be bombarded with demands: "Why don't you take me too?" I knew that a group session wouldn't be the same, but I thought it might be a worthwhile way to give all the kids a chance to express themselves through singing and to experience the enrichment of live music-making. It would also be — I hoped — a time to practice badly-needed social skills like taking turns, cooperation, respect, and so on.

Marilyn was willing. "But they're a handful, you know that," she warned with her usual mocking chuckle. I did know that. Lizzie's group, the Anthonites, were among the youngest — from six to ten years old — and most disturbed kids at St Mary's. Whole-group activities were notoriously difficult with them. Most had a background of wretched treatment by their parents, followed by repeated failures in foster homes. Their charts told dreary stories of being kicked out of schools, violent or sexual attacks on siblings, pre-school-age suicide attempts, fire-setting, depression, episodes of psychotic behavior, and a surprising frequency of medical problems and hospitalizations unrelated to abuse. More than half were freed for adoption — a euphemism meaning that either their parents had permanently abandoned them or that the court had terminated their parental rights, a step resulting only from the gravest abuse or neglect. Adoption was an unlikely miracle for these children. They were too old, too disturbed, too racially undesirable for most people looking for sons and daughters to love.

I arranged with Marilyn to come each Tuesday lunchtime. Once the meal was cleared away we'd sit around the tables in the kitchen and sing.

On the appointed day I came in for the first session, guitar case in hand and a list of songs in my mind. In the kitchen Marilyn and Rita were working hard to keep chaos at bay.

"George! It's your turn to clear!" George grinned without looking up and continued his project of smearing mashed potato and gravy around the edge of the table. At another table a fight was simmering, a continuation, I gathered, of something that had happened in school that morning. "You made me get in trouble, dickhead." "So? Dickhead yourself."

"Hey! It's Jo Salas!" yelled Tiahna, spotting me at the door. Sean jumped up and hurled himself at me, knocking me off balance. "Josephine!" called Lizzie plaintively from a table in the corner.

"Now, settle down, everyone, Jo's here to sing with you guys, remember, I told you?" Marilyn's voice cut through like a trombone. The children grew quiet.

I pulled up a chair, checking it for gravy, and took out the guitar. The kids swiveled towards me, curious. Marilyn and Rita positioned themselves strategically beside the wildest of them.

"Who knows this one?" I launched into "Oh Susannah." Some of them began to join in.

"What's a banjo?" said Edgar, interrupting. I explained.

"What's Alabama?" asked someone else. My explanations bogged down when we got to "It rained all night the day I left, the weather it was dry."

"The person in the song is just trying to be funny, I guess," I said lamely. "Let's try this one." The next one on my list had lyrics which couldn't be simpler:

Love somebody, yes I do
Love somebody but I won't tell who

The high notes were hard for most of the kids. Lizzie got there easily.

I was pleased that on the whole they were singing and apparently enjoying it. In between scoldings, Marilyn and Rita sang along, each now with a child in her lap. By the time the children had to line up at the door and return to school we'd got through about six songs, finishing up with a lusty rendition of "I've been working on the railroad." I was exhausted.

"So, not bad, Jo," said Marilyn. "The little darlings actually sang for you. They liked it. Think you'll come back?"

"Of course," I said. "Next week."

The next week she wasn't there. Rita and I tried our best to maintain order but neither of us radiated the authority that Marilyn so palpably embodied. Even though our first session had confirmed for me that singing together could indeed work, could be a chance for shared creativity and enrichment, it all depended on managing the group's behavior. Nothing I could offer had any point if the group collapsed in chaos.

Like dogs scenting fear the children sensed our growing anxiety and escalated their mayhem in response.

"OK, LaQiya, that's it!" yelled Rita after LaQiya had ignored her third request to stop tormenting Edgar. "Time out in the living room!"

"Fuck you!" said LaQiya, a chubby corn-rowed six-year-old with two teeth missing in front. Rita hauled her out amid a squeal of curses. "Jerkbutt! Cocksucker! Black pussy!" I hastily went on with another song. It was about fishing, one of their favorite activities:

You get a line and I'll get a pole
We'll go fishin' in the crawdad hole
Honey, sugarbaby mine

But the second verse broke down in renewed squabbles. It was like being inside a popcorn popper. The second I turned my attention to one eruption there were four more in four other directions. When Rita returned we looked at each other grimly.

"Kids, we're going to leave it at that today. Let's try again next week," I said. I felt defeated and disappointed.

"That's not fair!" "It wasn't my fault!" "He started it!" "She started it!" "They started it!" screamed the kids, all pointing at each other in righteous accusation.

I packed up my guitar. "It's time for school anyway," I said, backing out the door and leaving Rita to deal with them. I remembered my naive fantasy months earlier about singing with grateful little orphans. I'd learned by now how mistreated orphans are likely to behave.

When I arrived for the next session, they had a visitor, Brendan O'Brian, the director of childcare. Brendan was a big, warmhearted man with a presence like Santa Claus. The children loved him. Brendan twinkled at me from behind the cluster of kids entwining around him and cuddling in his large lap. "I hear you're going to sing with us," he said.

"Let's do the song about fishing," said LaQiya. "'Honey, sugarbaby mine'." The others were in agreement; no sign of the contentiousness of last week. They were eager to show Brendan all the songs we'd sung, surprising me with how much they had remembered in spite of the constant disruptions.

"You guys are great!" said Brendan. "Here, can I use the guitar?" I handed it to him. The kids slithered off his lap, expectant. "Come on, come on, come on, come baby, now," he sang, throwing his head back. The kids joined in, delighted. "Twist and shout, twist and shout!"

From week to week there was always just enough encouragement for me to keep going in spite of endless challenges and frustrations. The children were always eager and welcoming, which told me that singing together did indeed mean something to them. But I ended most of these sessions feeling rather like a guitar-playing Sisyphus. "You should just stop playing and yell at them," advised Rita. But I didn't like to yell and felt stubbornly sure that there must be a better way. Very gradually I learned what I could do to help the session run smoothly—the establishment of a consistent ritual with songs to greet each other and to say goodbye; the strategy of noting all requests and including them the following session instead of right away; letting them know clearly what my expectations of their behavior were; choosing songs that were both meaningful and easy for the children. After a while I learned how to modulate their wild volatility so that the group did not dissolve in chaos even when Marilyn was busy somewhere else, as she often was.

One day when we sang "Love somebody" Sean and Bailey changed the lyrics to "Hate somebody, yes I do, hate somebody but I won't say who." I ignored them, hoping the song wouldn't degenerate into insults and hostility. Thinking about it later, I realized how few children's songs there are that express anything other than happy or playful feelings. A rueful sadness sometimes, but anything stronger—rage, hate, fear, grief—is not to be found. So I wrote an angry song for them:

Sometimes I want to punch you
Right in your silly face
I want to cut you up into tiny little pieces
And get right out of this place

It was called "Mean and Ugly" and it quickly became one of the most frequently requested of the songs. Seeing the children's relish for these uncompromising lyrics, I worried that the staff might think that the song was an incitement to violence. I took Marilyn aside to talk about it. She cut me off. "You don't have to explain to me," she said. "I think it's great." Long afterwards, Bailey, now a big boy in another living unit, lost himself in rage at a staff member. Ricocheting in fury around the empty gym, he began to sing "Mean and Ugly" under his breath. "Sometimes I want to punch you"—leaping up to swipe at the basketball hoop—"right in your silly face"—kicking the cement walls—"I want to cut you up into tiny little pieces"—slamming a mat down on the floor as though it was a wrestling partner—"And get right out of this place." By the time he finished the second verse his anger had abated enough for him to slow down and talk to us.

I wrote another song for them, a song that had each child's name in it as well as a chorus that said:

Everybody's got a name
And none of them the same
Every name has got a face
Every face has got a place

The song gave each child a moment where her or his individuality was recognized, a proud moment of awareness both of self and of their place in this little community. Each line was echoed in a call-and-response pattern. The children liked this one too, and asked Marilyn to pin a copy of it to the kitchen bulletin board so they could sing it between sessions. Over time, as children left the group and others took their place, I rearranged the names to find new rhymes. Sometimes they'd squirm with momentary embarrassment as we sang their names: but, with occasional exceptions, they wanted to hear them. It meant something to them to have this public and positive acknowledgment.

I found a Valentine's Day song by Woody Guthrie, a set of whimsical little tunes by Malvina Reynolds, and the book of "Songs for Self-esteem" that I'd used with Lizzie. One of the songs was the "Put-Down Blues" — "I hate to hear what I'm doing wrong, every day of the year; I'd rather hear what I'm doing *right*, and where do I go from here." The children were enthusiastic about songs like "Old MacDonald" and "I've Been Working on the Railroad" (with raucous energy each time on "Fee, Fie, Fiddly-Eye-O"). A few of them especially loved "Over the Rainbow" and learned to sing it beautifully. I learned the importance of selecting songs which allowed several different levels of participation, from singing all the lyrics to joining in with just a "fill-in" or even just a sound or gesture. This flexibility made room for children in varying states of verbal development and emotional presence.

As was so often the case at St Mary's, logistics sometimes played against success: lunch might be delivered late from the central kitchen, the nurse might interrupt with a lengthy round of meds, half of the kids could be confined to their rooms as a result of earlier misdeeds, there might be a fire alarm just as we were getting started, and we'd all have to troop outside, snow or sweltering sun, to be counted and sent back in.

A couple of years later we re-configured the Anthonite singing sessions as an after-school activity on Fridays for the children who had been left behind while others went on reward trips or home visits. There were usually six or seven kids, forlorn after watching the others leave. They were not the same children I'd worked with in the kitchen, who had by now moved on to other groups or had been discharged.

The children were lounging in the living room watching television one day when I came in with the guitar. I studied them for a moment before interrupting them to turn off the set. There was Shade, a naughty puppy hiding a broken heart; Lydia, a razor-tongued critic of everyone around her, child or adult; tiny thumbsucking Ramiro; Elliott, a newcomer, still very shy in this strange place; Josiah, who spent the majority of his time in crisis; and sullen Tawan, just back from four weeks in a psychiatric hospital. For each of these kids, singing together held a promise or a possibility—the chance to join voices in song as human beings have done for eons; to express the love and pride and fear that stirred in their wounded and tender hearts; to recognize that others shared or sympathized with their emotion; to learn how enjoyable it can be to be part of a cooperative group; and the simple goal of joy, a profoundly healing experience in itself.

Tawan objected strenuously when I turned off the television set. He'd been in the hospital when the singing groups had begun two weeks earlier. "This is bullshit," he muttered, sitting with arms folded and pointedly ignoring the rest of us as we launched into singing. We began, as usual, with a hello song that I'd written for them:

Here we are, it's another day
Just one thing that I would like to say
Oh Lydia, and Josiah
Hello to you

We sang around the circle, some of the children joining in forthrightly when it was their turn to be named, others fidgeting with combined pleasure and shyness or shooting proud little glances at each other as they heard themselves named, two at a time. I knew they enjoyed this brief moment in the limelight: they'd made it clear that they wanted and expected this opening ritual each session. But Tawan held up a warning hand. "Don't sing my name." We didn't.

Elliott had requested "We are the world" at the previous session. He sang out with a fine, strong voice at odds with his fragile appearance, pleased with himself then startled by the others' attention.

Ramiro listened intently, removing his thumb to yell "Scooby doo!" at the right moment in another song, one that I'd written in collaboration with an older boy:

Love is a feeling that you have inside you
You know it's true
Love is a feeling that I have for you
Scooby doo!

I noted Ramiro's concentration and timing, an achievement for this child usually ruled by impulsiveness. Shade danced in her chair, holding up Marilyn's keys and shaking them like a maraca. She was doing well; in both previous sessions she'd had to be sent out when her wildness threatened to disrupt the group.

We sang our version of the chorus of "Alice's Restaurant" — "You can get anything you want..." "Remember, this is a magic restaurant," I told them. "You can have *anything* you want, food or anything else." The song gave each child in the circle a chance to voice a dream, whatever it might be.

They contributed lines: "I want to live wit' my sister," said Shade. "I want to be the richest person in the world," said Elliott. "I want to see my baby brother," said Lydia.

Ramiro took his thumb out again and squeaked "I want pizza, hamburger and soda." Tawan said nothing. We ended with a contemplative goodbye song, again with all the names in it. The goodbye song offered another moment of recognition for each child and helped them to prepare for the transition to whatever was to be next in their day.

I glanced at Tawan, who avoided my eye. I decided to include his name this time. He didn't object.

I knew by now that the attitude of the staff made an enormous difference in any group activity. It was a given that other staff members needed to be present when I or any therapist was working with a group, for safety as well as logistics. But beyond this pragmatic need there was the question of support for the activity itself: a staff member who considered that singing together was worthwhile would communicate that view to the children simply by his or her demeanor, with the result that the children were far more likely to take part in an enjoyable and constructive way. Even more subtle, but unmistakable, was a staff member's fundamental attitude toward the children themselves. I sensed a distinction, never discussed, between staff whose treatment of the children was based on profound respect for them as fellow human beings and those who believed at heart that the kids were in some way irrevocably different and inferior. This division existed at every level throughout the institution; there were teachers, therapists, administrators, childcare staff, even secretaries and maintenance workers, on both sides.

I tried hard to encourage the Anthonite staff and teach them how they could most help the children during the music sessions. It made a difference, especially to the people whose distance was the result of shyness or uncertainty rather than scorn. It was gratifying to see them relax and enjoy themselves, cuddling on the couch with the children and letting themselves join in with the silliest of songs.

One day I came in to find Shade and four boys, including one who was visiting from another group. "Watch out, they're wired," said Phil, the child care worker on duty. He was right. The boys were excited by their visitor, Jamel, an older boy from upstairs in the Jeromist group. Jamel had decreed before I appeared that group singing was not at all cool. The others were following his lead by being as outrageous and disruptive as they could, farting, shouting, giggling, complaining loudly about songs which last week they had been delighted to sing. In a sense Jamel was right that our repertoire was childish: I had often been struck at how these streetwise children, so ready in general to deride anything that was "country" when only "city" could be cool, nevertheless were hungry for songs that were close in their simplicity to nursery rhymes. As far as I could gather, few if any of them had had parents who sang to them. I wondered if they instinctively recognized what they had missed and sought to fill in the emotional and linguistic gaps left by their disrupted early childhood.

Phil, no more enthusiastic about singing than Jamel, made it clear that he was not about to help, sitting in the back of the room and ostentatiously unwrapping a candy bar. I decided to respond to the general mayhem by challenging their self-control—stopping a song in the middle and waiting for silence before continuing, whispering lyrics to them and inviting them to sing them very quietly, making the hand motions of a song while mouthing the words without sound. This strategy worked, but it took a while.

At one point I put down my guitar. "I'm just not having fun," I said. "I don't know if I really want to be here today."

"Staff aren't supposed to have fun," retorted Jamel.

"Why not?" I answered.

He couldn't think of a reason. In spite of himself he got more and more involved, and the others followed suit.

Tawan, who had barely begun to emerge from his stony silence at these sessions, was revealing himself now as someone who could be as rude and silly as the next boy. Earlier in the week in a treatment team meeting I had heard that Tawan had seriously injured his teacher in class. She was still at home, trying to recover from the emotional shock as well as from the injury itself. Tawan had shown pride rather than remorse. "I'll hit the bitch worse when she gets back," he'd said. I thought of this as I watched him enjoy himself in the only way he knew, being gross and obstreperous. Tawan was only ten, but already big. The incident with his teacher was one of many outbreaks of violence without remorse. The adult he was in danger of becoming was not hard to imagine.

It was rare to feel the hopelessness that Tawan aroused in me. Sadness was a daily experience, working with children whose lives were so tragic. But almost always there was the sense that change was possible. I hoped I was wrong about Tawan.

The Anthonite singing groups became a regular aspect of life in this living unit, something that newcomers were initiated into by children who'd been taking part for months or years. We built a core repertoire of songs, adapting some of the old ones and adding new ones. The groups went more and more smoothly within the steady framework of a consistent sequence and expectations. The structure and content of the songs themselves gave the children a space in which urgent emotional needs could be expressed and addressed.

At one point we scheduled the singing sessions for the spell between dinner and bedtime, so that the kids could be in their pajamas with all their "routines" done—teeth-brushing, face-washing, clothes in the laundry basket—and go straight from singing to bed. It meant staying late each Monday night, but I didn't mind. I liked the quietness of the building when all the children were back in their living units having dinner and most of the staff had gone home.

Perhaps it was the different vibration of the evening, or the semi-darkened room, or the children's tiredness after their jangled day, or the kindly presence of Ted and Kurt, the childcare workers usually on duty—for whatever reasons, the evening sing-alongs were generally a delight, free of the strife that tended to plague the earlier groups.

In this intimate atmosphere the children used the songs to express things of great importance to them. On the evening of Martin Luther King's birthday I taught them "We shall overcome," telling them about all the people who had sung this song together to change the world. I invited the children to make up lines about how they might like to change their own world. They were quiet, thinking.

"Families won't take drugs," said Rashid, whose parents had abandoned him as a result of their addiction. We sang:

Families won't take drugs
Families won't take drugs
Families won't take drugs some day
Oh deep in my heart, I do believe
We shall overcome some day

There were other contributions: we will have no violence; families will live forever. Caridad, snuggling on Ted's lap, called out, "We will all go home."

I thought about Dr King and his dream as I looked around at the children, most of them wounded by our racist social and economic order. Still so much to overcome.

We did another song which invited the kids to fill in the line "I felt..." after a different scenario in each verse.

I got a new game on Christmas day
My friends asked to borrow it so they could play
They didn't bring it back until weeks had gone by
Pieces were missing and they didn't say why
I felt...

"Insulted!" yelled Ogden, who had been quiet so far. He had

returned from a home visit the day before with his front teeth broken. He was upset and self-conscious but he wouldn't talk about it. The social workers hadn't been able to reach his parents to find out what had happened.

Next was an action song about the treacherous crocodile who ate his foolishly trusting lady passenger. At the last line, "And the smile was on the crocodile," the kids stretched their faces into crocodile smiles, looking around at each other and giggling. It was their favorite part of the song. Ogden brandished his scary-looking teeth.

"You wanna know what happened?" he asked. "My dad crashed the car because he was drunk and I slammed into the front and my teeth got broke."

Five

HARMONY AND DISSONANCE

Rafael, my "tornado," was a musically talented child. He sang easily in tune and could hold harmony parts, he had a sophisticated sense of rhythm, and loved music passionately; he wanted to play, sing and hear it as much as he possibly could. A number of the other children I worked with, including Lizzie, had a similarly strong affinity for music. Like the professional musicians I knew, these children had both the need and the ability to make music the way a bird has the need and ability to fly.

Music therapy generally emphasizes the process of music-making rather than skill development or performance. The professional literature explores music's accessibility and importance to all human beings rather than to the talented minority. But I came to realize that for children like Rafael, talent was very significant indeed. Their talent, or musical intelligence, meant first of all that they were strongly drawn to take part in music, and to take part consistently, an important thing for children whose motivation for any kind of therapy was often erratic. It also gave them an arena—for some, the only such arena—in which they knew themselves to be competent and successful. Most of the gifted but disturbed children I worked with seemed more "normal"—more communicative and connected, more in possession of themselves, more "civilized"—while engaged with music. Over time, some of their healthier behavior appeared outside of music sessions as well. Lizzie and another child, Billy Gaston (he appears in chapter seven), who grew worse to the point of being discharged into long-term hospitalization, remained ordered and productive in music even as the rest of their lives fell apart.

It was also clear to me that the familiar distinction between "musical" and "unmusical" was a fiction. We tend to assume, in modern Western culture, that music is the domain only of the gifted, and that the gifted are few. Through recording technology our ears are now so accustomed to perfection that people with more modest ability or lacking training seldom even attempt to play or sing, denying themselves the great joy of music-making, whether shared or solo. It is a loss which many feel while not questioning the assumptions on which it is based. I have met dozens of adults who admit with sharp regret that they never sing because as children they were told by some uninspired music teacher that they shouldn't. Even so, the love of music remains, expressed only by listening.

People in some non-Western cultures seem quite free of this limiting assumption. Speaking of non-European music traditions in his book *Music, Society, Education*, musicologist Christopher Small says: "The music is not performed as 'me', the composer or performer, addressing 'you', the audience, but as all of us, of whom some may be musicians and some not, taking part in the common ritual or activity....The idea of a concert or performance in our sense of the word is thus virtually unknown." In African and many Asian communities as well as others, music-making, singing, and dancing are felt to be integral to life and accessible to everyone, though at the same time special talents and devoted training may be highly valued. I remember attending a gathering of about a dozen Nepali language teachers where one of them proposed making music after dinner. Everyone took turns singing solo verses of traditional songs without a trace of self-consciousness. Not all were "good" singers. The ones with beautiful voices were listened to with special pleasure. But no one said "I don't sing" or apologized sheepishly for their lack of talent.

In my informal observation of both children and adults, there seems to be a bell curve of natural musical ability, with a few highly endowed people at one end, and, at the other, a small number who find it difficult to discern pitch or rhythm. The middle holds the majority: people whose musicality will develop readily with cultural and educational support. The strength of the drive to make music generally parallels the degree of talent, though there are exceptions in both directions, with less-gifted people who yearn to play and perform and—less common—highly-gifted people who are not especially interested in pursuing music.

Besides the outstandingly gifted Billys and Rafaels at St Mary's there were other, more averagely-talented children who also benefited from music therapy and for similar reasons. The singing groups that I led in the Anthonites and other living units served children who were not highly talented but perfectly capable of engaging productively in vocal and instrumental music, given opportunity and encouragement. In one-to-one sessions such children also responded to music with focus and enjoyment. Music was a way to express themselves, to find a sense of strength, to connect, to be creative, to participate productively in a social world. They shared the pleasure and satisfaction of making music, if without the passionate drive of the true musician.

Motivation, in fact, was the most significant predictor of the effectiveness of music therapy. Regardless of natural ability, if a child *wanted* to play and sing, music was a fertile place for him to grow in whatever direction he needed to, towards hope or relationship or the strengthening of a sense of order, or away from despair and isolation. All of the St Mary's children stood to gain from the therapeutic promise of music, but it was those who were actively attracted to music who gained the most.

Sometimes the instruments themselves effected healing. The human soul needs love, needs to be attached to at least one other fellow being, as urgently as the body needs food and water. Most of the children at St Mary's were struggling with ruptured, sometimes poisoned attachments to their parents and the consequent mistrust of other possible relationships. For some, it helped, at least for a while, to love an object which had no power to hurt or disappoint them because it was inanimate.

Marcel was eleven, an affable white boy with a stringy body and a benign smile. In one of his early sessions I showed him the autoharp, a many-stringed folk instrument with buttons which you push to make chords while strumming with the other hand.

"I've got fifteen of these at home," said Marcel, playing it experimentally. "What did you say it's called?"

"The autoharp."

"Oh, yes, the autoheart."

That was its name from then on: a few months later it had become

"Mr Autoheart." Mr Autoheart was Marcel's ally, his love, both the embodiment and the recipient of his strongest emotions. Marcel seemed gentle, free of the bristling physical anger that many of the other children carried around with them. But the records said that he had savagely beaten his younger brother during the years they lived together, and his destructive impulses were apparently of concern to himself.

"What would happen if I dropped Mr Autoheart?" he asked one day.

"It would probably be OK, especially in here where it's carpeted."

"What if I dropped it on cement?"

"It might get chipped, or some of the strings might break, I guess."

"What if I smashed it onto the concrete steps outside?"

"Well, then you'd break the wood itself, and it probably couldn't be fixed."

"No! No! I'd fix him myself, wouldn't t I, Mr Autoheart?" He hugged the instrument and rocked it like a baby. "Even if you were in the garbage, I'd get you right out and fix you up, wouldn't I?"

Marcel was convinced that the autoharp reciprocated his love. He made up a song about it: "I am Mr Autoheart and this is my nice friend Marcel." It was indeed a friend to him at times of particular anxiety. One day his teacher spoke to me about his poor behavior in school, which she attributed to his mother's failure to appear for a long-planned visit. The moment he was in the Space Room Marcel opened the closet where the autoharp was kept and drew it out, talking incessantly to it.

"You missed me, didn't you, yes you did, and I missed you too. Did you think I wasn't coming? Of course I was coming, I came as soon as I could" and so on. He seemed hardly aware that I was there. "I'll always love you, you know that, don't you, you're my own little Mr Autoheart, I'm gonna take care of you no matter what. Don't you worry, little Mister." He cradled it, drawing his hand gently across the strings so that they sounded in a chromatic whisper.

When it was time for Marcel to be discharged—to a group home, since his family was far from ready to take care of him—he was full of fears about how the autoharp would survive without him. "Can't I take him with me? I'm the only one he loves." But I couldn't let him take such an expensive instrument. I tried to assure him that I and others would be as careful with it as he had been. We spent some time making a dulcimer from a kit, something that he'd be able to keep and play in his new home.

"It's not the same," he said but by the time he left he was fond of the little cardboard dulcimer too. "It's country but I still like it. Her. It's a her, I think."

The significance of musical affinity in healing led me to work with three talented siblings, the Lewis children. It was a rarity to have siblings at St Mary's, and unprecedented to have three at a time. Exceptionally bright and physically beautiful, all three were struggling with depression and disturbed behavior as a consequence of sexual abuse by their father and physical violence from their mother. The children's father, Manning Lewis, had alliteratively named his children Melinda, Miles, and Mandy, and had persuaded his wife to change her name to Mara. Now he was in prison. It had been Melinda who had finally ended the years of incest, seeing that he was drawing Mandy, the youngest, into the terrible web that held the rest of them immobilized. Melinda couldn't forgive herself for breaking up the family.

I'd decided to put all the Lewises into the same group, in spite of warnings from Alice, their social worker, because both Miles and Melinda had talked to me with longing about how they used to sing together before the family had been separated. Although the difficulties of my own childhood were mild in comparison, I remembered well how my sisters' voices blending with mine in four-part harmony had been an important counterbalance to our hardships. I wanted to offer the Lewis children a chance to connect with something healthy about their family—to remember that their life together had been more than its burden of shame and damage.

It lasted for about a year, until Melinda was discharged to a group home, but it never became easy. Miles was curdled with a suppressed rage which seeped out constantly. He fidgeted with noisy instruments when we were trying to talk or sing. He complained about every activity, yet insisted he wanted to keep coming. Mandy, six years old, behaved more like a toddler, dogging Melinda with demands for physical contact. She stuttered badly, finding relief only when she sang. The disappearance of her stutter in singing excited me at first until I learned that it is a well-known phenomenon and does not usually lead to fluency in spoken language. Melinda's eagerness for music was often sabotaged by her depression and frequent stomach aches. She and Miles infuriated each other. Both were disgusted by Mandy.

Woven through all this anger and sadness was their love for each other, as well as their creative passion. Once in a while there was a clearing when the children found each other in the music.

"Do you remember that song, something about Kentucky?" said Melinda one day. "Mommy sang it to us."

They sat together in the middle of the room, Miles and Melinda with guitars on their laps, animated as the song came back to them line by line:

Oh we'll sing one song for my old Kentucky home
For my old Kentucky home far away

"We could sing it to Mom next time she visits!" said Melinda, her pale cheeks flushed. Mara, under punishment for her ambiguous role in the sexual abuse and for her own violence toward the children, was permitted only to see them once a month in supervised visits.

"We could, I guess," said Miles, unsure.

"Yeah!" said Mandy, wriggling with excitement.

Melinda reminded me about the song as soon as I picked them up for the next session. They worked hard on it, coaching Mandy on the words of the chorus. Their three voices fell into an easy blending, tuneful and pleasurable to hear. They smiled at each other as they sang. Melinda experimented with a harmony line. A stranger peeking in the big window would have seen three attractive and gifted siblings, not survivors of a tragic family.

On the day of their mother's next visit the children stood together in the visiting room, Melinda holding Mandy's hand. They'd asked me to accompany them on guitar. Mara's lip quivered as her children sang.

"Oh, oh, my," she said when they'd finished. "You remembered that old song?" She wiped her eyes.

"Don't cry, Mommy," said Mandy, hugging her. Melinda and Miles stood quietly beside me, watching.

I'd been fascinated and repelled at the idea of meeting Mara, a woman who had apparently failed to intervene while her husband stole her children's innocence and their chance of ordinary happiness. Alice had claimed loudly that she must be either evil or stupid. No one knew to what extent she herself might have been a prisoner and victim.

In the visiting room, Mara seemed neither evil nor stupid but bereft, a wasted woman. I tried but couldn't imagine what it might feel like to have lost the chance to mother one's children.

For a while I saw Melinda in individual sessions as well. She wanted to learn the guitar, and I lent her one of the new instruments that I'd acquired for the program. Musical and motivated as she was, though, it seemed difficult for her to overcome her habitual apathy. She would forget to bring the guitar with her, or tell me languidly that she hadn't practiced. In the sessions she'd sit drooped over the guitar, sighing and withdrawn. She learned chords readily but refused to practice them, impatient to move on to new ones and annoyed with me if I pressed her. I wrote chart after chart for the songs she requested, only to have her say that she'd lost them. She was full of physical complaints—her throat hurt, her fingers hurt, her long nails hurt on the fingerboard. "You could trim them, Melinda. Guitarists always have short fingernails on their left hands," I said, showing her mine. She looked at me witheringly. "Are you crazy? Do you know how long it took to get them this long?"

Melinda was moving swiftly into adolescence. Most of her creativity went into the careful assembling of a new persona for herself, a kind of juvenile Madonna. She wore clothes as sexually provocative as she thought she could get away with and was frequently sent back upstairs to change when she appeared at school in a body-revealing outfit and heavy make-up. To the particular horror of Hilda, the volunteer religion teacher, Melinda wore rosaries and crucifixes as jewelry. Hilda was one of her enemies, because of Melinda's inquiring intelligence as well as her style of dress. She told me that she'd asked Hilda why, if God was all-powerful, he had allowed her father do what he did. "You'll burn in hell forever for asking that question," was Hilda's theological response. Hilda's fire-and-brimstone religious instruction drove children more fragile than Melinda to shocking nightmares. I couldn't understand why she was permitted to work at St Mary's.

Listening to public radio on the way to work one morning I heard of the accidental death of someone I loved, a well-known musician and writer. I was still trying to contain my shock and sorrow when I came to pick up Melinda for her 9:30 session. Stirred from her usual anomie by my red eyes and lack of a smile, she asked me what was wrong. I told her, knowing I couldn't pretend. She was warm, concerned. She wanted to know more about my friend, how I had known her, how she had died. In spite of my sadness I was pleased and touched to see this other side of Melinda, a person who after all shared the world with others.

It did not last long. Her remoteness came back as the session continued. It was always the same with Melinda—a few moments of connection, eye contact, warmth, conversation, then apathy and distance again.

The Lewises were among the majority of children at St Mary's for whom sexual abuse had been a factor, in some cases the main factor, in their mental illness. The staff estimated that at least half of the boys and most of the girls had been abused sexually, usually by a father, step-father or mother's boyfriend, more rarely by a mother or aunt. LaQiya, the Anthonites' cuddly six-year-old troublemaker, was the survivor of sexual abuse so extreme that even the long-time staff, used to dreadful stories, were shaken. As a one-year-old baby she had been raped by her mother's boyfriend. It had taken many hours of surgery to reconstruct her tiny body. Even so, her suffering was not over: she had been assaulted again at four years old by another male relative.

Learning a history such as this at a meeting or in the medical records, I was shocked and sickened. Then I had to collect myself and continue the day's work. But at night, the rush of the day over and my own children safely asleep, I lay awake haunted and heartbroken. LaQiya, Lizzie, the Lewises, Tiahna whose drug-addicted mother prostituted her as an infant, Jermain, raped and burnt by his father—I kept hearing of more. I had never come close to such horror before. I searched in my mind to find a way to encompass it. How could anyone behave with such monstrous brutality to a child?

The visceral disgust and grief that kept me awake those first weeks and months was to do with the exploitation and cruelty that these children had already endured. As time went on, I saw more fully the permanent damage that had been done to them. For some, like Lizzie or LaQiya, their lives had been destroyed almost as surely as if they had been murdered. The Lewises perhaps had a chance, thanks to Melinda's courage in halting the abuse.

The victims of the sex abusers were often prematurely sexualized, obsessed with sex. "Do you hump your husband?" LaQiya asked me after inquiring conversationally if I was married. She was stimulated by the slightest thought of sex, or by her own body. It was grotesque and disturbing to see a small child so familiar with the sensations of sex. Some of the girls were tormented by longing for the man who had violated them, who might have loved and flattered them as well. They blamed themselves, remembering gratification as well as anguish. As they grew toward adolescence the distorted patterns of their emotions and their sexuality led them to develop relationships with males that mimicked the one that had so destructively formed them. We saw them pulled inexorably toward a debased womanhood built on the conviction that sex was all they could offer in exchange for love or safety. For the most traumatized of the children, neither time nor all the expertise and devotion of the St Mary's staff could undo the devastation.

We learned with grief and outrage that not even our treatment center could keep the children safe from harm. A little more than a year after I came to St Mary's a teacher overheard two boys talking in class about Dr Fisher, how he always touched their private parts, and how they hated it. The clinical staff investigated and found out that indeed these boys and perhaps others had been repeatedly molested by the clinical director. They confronted Marcus Fisher. He did not deny it.

I was in turmoil. Marcus was my first and strongest connection at St Mary's. I liked him. He seemed devoted to the children, an intelligent and compassionate man. He respected my work, and in his casual way had been my main supporter. How could he also be a monster who would betray the trust of his staff and of these fragile children, already so damaged by cruel and exploitive adults? I couldn't reconcile these two realities.

Other people at St Mary's seemed to have no difficulty in detesting him unequivocally. Dr. Thody, stepping in as acting clinical director, brought the therapists together in the visiting room, hoping that we could help each other come to terms with what had happened. We crowded into the small room, perching on the blue couch and upholstered dining chairs.

"I always thought there was something weird about him," said one of the social workers, venom in her voice. There were murmurs of concurrence.

"I could kill the bastard," said someone else.

"But he's still the same person we all knew," I protested. I was still in a maelstrom of shock and confusion. "I can't suddenly hate him when I liked him just a few days ago." No one agreed with me.

But my own compassion ebbed away as I saw the harm done to the children. Living through the aftermath of this cataclysm was a nightmare for everyone at St Mary's. The children all learned about it, in spite of attempts at containment. They were deeply troubled, their precarious security badly shaken. There were constant crisis incidents, violence, running away, suicide threats. Reporters waited at the stone pillars day after day, but we were instructed not to speak to them. No one wanted to anyway. We were ashamed and bruised, a family tainted by one member's wrongdoing. Dr Fisher was charged in criminal court. Some of the staff were involved as witnesses. The boys had to be questioned, traumatizing them further. One of them was Vern, whom I'd been working with for several months. He became depressed and self-destructive, blaming himself for Dr Fisher being fired. His earlier progress toward health and imminent discharge was reversed. It was a very long time before we saw Vern smiling and confident again.

Six

"DO MY STORY!"

With the encouragement and financial support of Mike Murray, the school principal, I arranged to bring in other members of Playback Theatre to do a show in the gym. I was sure the children would like Playback Theatre, but I was concerned about the riot factor, knowing from other events that even when they were enjoying something they could easily overpower it with their raucous enthusiasm. At any moment, too, there was the possibility of one or more of them succumbing to emotional crisis—"going off," in St Mary's parlance. It was impossible to predict what stories and feelings might be stirred by our performance. I oriented the others as best I could. I was going to be the musician. Jonathan, my husband and fellow-playbacker, would cope with the "conductor" role, Playback's onstage emcee.

The children spilled into the gym, intrigued to see it transformed with our characteristic stage set-up. Two chairs stood on one side for the conductor and a storyteller. Near them was a wooden structure hung with bright pieces of fabric, the only props, along with plastic milk crates, that we used in this improvisational format. On the other side of the stage area was an array of instruments: that was my station. Four actors sat on the milk crates across the back of the stage, ready to be chosen as characters in the children's stories. Upstage, a big exercise mat stood on its side, making a tall screen above which our "puppets"— an assortment of odd objects like a giant pair of wooden scissors, a doll, a detergent bottle and a snorkel—would appear and act out some of the stories.

We launched into the show with a song and an introduction of the performers. "We know her!" yelled the children when I stood up and said my name. Jonathan began to explain to them that Playback is about our own real stories, not other people's stories from books or television or the movies. But it was soon clear that little explanation was needed. As soon as they realized that we were inviting them to tell us what had really happened to them, hands shot up all over the room. There were far more stories than the four we had time for—José's story about being scared by a ghost in a cave, Sean's about buying candy on his birthday and eating it all himself, Amy's story about the kind childcare worker who told her a fairytale at bedtime. LaQiya told a story about saying goodbye to her mother when she left to live in a group home. The puppets acted out this one, poignant in spite of the absurdity of the objects themselves. The children were quiet. I played music for each story. It was the first time that I'd brought my violin to St Mary's.

When it was over the children lingered talking to us until they had to line up and return to their groups. I helped carry the equipment out to the cars and waved goodbye to Jonathan and the actors. I was happy that it had gone so well. There was obviously a place for Playback at St Mary's. I knew I was going to do more.

I ran a series of training sessions for anyone on the staff who wanted to learn drama techniques, including Playback Theatre, to use with the children. A mixed group of people came, childcare staff, psychologists and social workers, recreation workers and several of the creative arts therapists who were by now working part time at St Mary's. Some had been present at the Playback show in the gym. When the series was over, they wanted to learn more about Playback. They were excited about the idea of eventually performing for the children.

We arranged to meet in the Space Room on Thursdays at lunchtime. With people arriving late from a last-minute crisis with a child or from running uptown to pick up a sandwich, our time together was scant. Still, they learned the basics of Playback —the protocol of enacting a scene so that the teller's story was held in a clear sequence, the short dance-like form called fluid sculptures and other brief ways to respond to an audience member's comment. They learned to be open to being chosen by the teller to play any role, from the teller herself to a neglectful parent or a moldy hamburger. They practiced being bold and expressive; they learned to listen deeply to the teller so that they could absorb both meaning and details; they developed the aesthetic sense of story through which a raw-edged piece of life might be transformed into theatre.

For the people in the group (and it soon felt like a group, as we told and enacted our own stories together) these lunchtime rehearsals became an oasis in the week, when the Space Room door closed firmly on the pressures of the job and the minefields of institutional politics. In the intimacy and fun of our meetings, the usual hard edges of department and hierarchy meant little. Others joined us, including Abel Hauser, one of the administrators. He'd told me once that he'd taken an improv class as a student and loved it. When he heard that a Playback group was rehearsing in the Space Room he asked if he could come along. As a Playback actor Abel was attentive and playful. His elevated status became irrelevant, though it seemed to me that a few of the others especially relished pushing him around in some of our physical warm-ups. (Like almost every powerful person at St Mary's, Abel was a big man, more than capable of holding his own.)

After a couple of months we felt ready to act out stories for the kids. As a group our skills were still crude, especially compared to the long-established original Playback Theatre company. But this fledgling, as-yet unnamed company had the advantage of knowing the children. Our intimacy with them would be our strength. Our polish as a performing team would grow, I hoped.

We met for our first show, excited and a little apprehensive. Fifteen kids scrambled into the gym, chattering their way to the folding chairs waiting in curving rows. A pair of large scoop lamps bathed the stage area in warm light. I stood in front of the children holding up my hands for quietness. They settled down and we began.

"How's your day been so far?" I asked.

"Bad!"

"Better than yesterday."

"I had to go to the crisis room."

"Lovable!" Calvin called out.

We acted out their comments in high-energy "fluid sculptures," adding sound and movement one by one to express the teller's feeling. The kids roared with delight.

Doreen, a plump, sweet-faced girl from the Teresian group, came to the teller's chair with the first story.

"It's about when my dog bit me," she said. She told the story of the mean dog, and the comfort she received from her mother and sister; both of them, I knew, long disappeared from her life. She chose Abel to play the dog, and he caused a near-riot when he pretended to pee against a piece of furniture and got spanked for it. The actors onstage waited out the screams of laughter so that they could show the tenderness of the moment between Doreen and her mother.

"Do my story! Do my story!" shouted five or six kids as soon as Doreen sat down.

My hope with Playback Theatre was to give the children a chance to tell their stories—to provide Playback's accessible stage as a forum where they could speak and be heard. I knew that they had remarkable stories to tell, that they were full of lively response to the world around them, and that in the rough-and-tumble of institutional life there were few opportunities for them to be heard other than in one-on-one therapy sessions. I thought that the ritual of Playback might prove a strong enough frame—even in this environment—for the children to bear witness in front of their peers.

Although our performances followed the traditional Playback format of tellers coming forward to tell and watch a story, we learned quickly to adapt it so that it worked for this special audience. We found that the children responded better to acting that was literal and concrete rather than metaphorical. Extra attention to opening and ending shows was called for. We sang with the children at the beginning to settle them into receptiveness and keep them occupied as latecomers straggled in. As the show ended we allowed time for verbal sharing, more singing, or art activities. More children wanted to be tellers than we had time for, and our closing activities gave the disappointed ones a chance to express a small part of the story they didn't tell.

In spite of occasional frustration at not telling their stories, the children were delighted to come to the shows, which they thought of as a treat, not therapy.

Soon, teachers in St Mary's school invited us to do shows in their small classrooms. In one classroom performance, six-year-old Courtney told a nightmare about a witch who came to her while she was asleep and put horrible stuff on her nails and pricked her skin.

"What was the scariest thing, Courtney?"

"I'm scared I'll be like the witch."

During the enactment she yelled at the witch: "I'm over here!" I reminded her that Diane, the actor she'd chosen, was being Courtney in the story, that she herself was just watching. She was very excited. I held her closely on my knee. When it was over, I asked her if she'd like to make up a different ending for her story. It was at first hard for her to understand the possibility I was offering. Then she got it. Her eyes lit up. "I want to kill the witch, and I want my mom to hug me and say 'Good girl.'" With satisfaction she watched this amended scenario acted out.

Gary, who'd been full of scathing complaints earlier, wanted to be the next teller. But when he came to the chair, he didn't have a story. It wasn't unusual for children to long for the experience of being a teller while being not at all clear about what they wanted to tell. It was our job to find a story, however minimal, in whatever elements they could offer.

"Who's someone who might be in your story?" I asked Gary.

"My grandma," he responded immediately. I had heard that Gary's grandmother had died recently after a long illness. Soon a story emerged about the time she had entrusted him and his brother to go to the store for her. "She wasn't sick, she just too busy. We got everything and we gave her some change and she was real pleased."

We acted out the story, Gary calling out additional details from the side as he remembered them. "She wanted *soup!*" he yelled. Without missing a beat, the teller's actor added soup to the grocery items he was putting in his imaginary basket.

"Thank you for telling us about your grandma, Gary," I said when the scene was over.

"Thank you for acting my story," he said, peaceful and gracious.

Two classes crowded into Hunter's classroom for a Playback show. Halfway through, Rogelio slipped through the door and picked his way carefully to a chair. He looked wretched. He raised his hand. "Please?" he begged. I waved him to the chair beside me.

"It's my birthday," he said, but his cast-down eyes made it clear that this was not going to be a story about celebration. He told us that he'd just come from a birthday lunch with his mother and siblings, preceded by a family therapy session in which his mother had screamed at him. Some of us had met his mother, a woman of explosive mood and capricious behavior. She'd stormed out of the therapy room, Rogelio said, threatening to go home instead of staying for the planned birthday party, then reappeared, full of apologies, ready for lunch. But lunch was even worse. Everyone was angry. Rogelio lost his temper, too, when his little sister smeared birthday cake all over her face. "The only good thing was I knew we were having a Playback show and I could tell a story about it," he said.

He chose Prue, a psychologist in the Playback group, to play his mother. It was hard for her. Her personal desire to help got in the way and prompted loving, motherly messages such as Rogelio's mother would never say: "I understand how you feel, honey. But it's not OK to yell at Mommy."

Rogelio looked at me when the scene was over. "My mom doesn't talk like that."

We tried it again and Prue did better. "I'm *outta* here! You kids make me sick!" she screamed.

"Yeah," said Rogelio with a sigh. "That's what it was like." I asked him if he'd like to see it turn out differently—a Playback "transformation." But he didn't. It was enough, this time, to be able to tell what happened and know that he'd been heard.

Acting out the children's stories was often emotionally taxing for the Playback actors. Hearing about cruelty and grief directly from a young teller herself or himself was different from reading a medical record or sitting in a treatment team meeting. Sometimes an actor couldn't resist playing the kind of parent she wished the child had really had. But the greater gift for the teller was to show his story as he told it, no matter how sad, no matter how hard for the performer. Only then could the child feel seen, heard, affirmed. We learned to put our own feelings to the side until later when we could comfort each other in the privacy of the Space Room.

A couple of months later Rogelio offered another story. "It's about my home visit." He seemed a lot happier than on the day of his birthday.

"I remember your birthday story, Rogelio," I said. "On a scale of one to ten how would you rate this one?"

He grinned. "It's a ten." During his visit, he told us, his mother wanted to sleep in the afternoon and asked him to watch his little sister. Rogelio planted 5-year-old Karina in front of the television to watch Barney (the audience supplied the Barney song during the enactment with suitable sarcasm—the show's syrupy sentimentality was not lost on them) so that he could search for the Christmas presents that he knew must be hidden somewhere. He was successful—and thrilled with what he found—but he dropped one and woke his mother. She was furious. "I'll take everything back to the store!" she yelled. Rogelio's older brother came home at that moment and calmed things down by taking Rogelio out to a movie.

"So did she take everything back?"

"No! I looked again last weekend!"

In Leah's classroom, nine-year-old Ernestine's hand shot up as soon as I asked for a story, but I passed over her to Omar, whose hand was up as well. I was remembering an earlier time when Ernestine had been the teller. An angular little girl with darting eyes, she was one of the children who sailed close to psychosis. Her story a couple of months ago had been chaotic and without discernible relationship to reality. After Omar's story was over, Ernestine's hand was in the air again, waving urgently. Inwardly crossing my fingers, I invited her to the teller's chair.

"What's your story about, Ernestine?"

"It's about how I became an artist." she said. She was emphatic and clear. I listened, moved. She went on to tell, with perfect cogency, how she had started on the artist's path when she was five, thanks to a helpful teacher. "And I've been an artist ever since," she finished triumphantly.

Ernestine watched the scene intently. "Yes, that's right," she said turning to me when it was over. She was smiling broadly, delighted to share this sense of herself with all of us in the room.

Like all Playback audiences, the children told stories about anything that was important to them. Sometimes a story revealed an aspect of the grievous history that had brought the child to St Mary's —stories about a drug-addicted mother, an abusive stepfather, violence on the streets of home. It was clear that telling and watching such a story helped in comprehending a painful reality, and that letting others know about it lightened the burden of carrying such pain alone. But we neither encouraged nor discouraged the children from telling such stories. We conveyed our openness to whatever they wished to tell. We felt certain that there was a different and equally important healing taking place when the story was about a reward trip to get pizza, being chosen as someone's friend, or, like Doreen, remembering the support and companionship of family members who may no longer have been available. Such a story was an affirmation to the child herself and to the people in her world that she was a person with success and happiness in her life as well as trouble.

For Courtney, Gary, Rogelio, and Ernestine, there were somewhat different healing outcomes from telling and seeing their stories. For Courtney, it was a way to gain mastery over a troubling dream, first by seeing it externalized and physically separate from herself, and then by the opportunity to re-imagine the scenario. In Playback we call this imagined outcome a "transformation" and it's always generated by the teller, in response to the conductor's invitation after the scene is first played as it happened. Sometimes a child might need help in grasping such a profoundly creative possibility, and then the conductor may offer a "for example" or two. But it is only the teller's own imagined scene that is acted out.

For Gary, telling a story about his recently-deceased grandmother was a healing chance to remember her as she was in life. In the company of others, he honored her and his relationship with her—a primary function of any mourning ritual. Knowing that he could very soon tell a Playback story about his miserable birthday lunch helped Rogelio to live through the experience. Ernestine's story claimed the part of her that was creative and functioning. It was also an articulation of inner life unlikely to take place in any other context at St Mary's.

Whatever the content of the stories, the most therapeutic effect of all was the experience of being heard, fully, respectfully, and without analysis or judgment. Interpretation in the psychological sense is not constructive in Playback Theatre, even in clinical applications. Playback

Theatre works like art or dream, presenting images, patterns, associations, allusions that are best comprehended on their own terms. The source of Playback Theatre's potency as a healing force is its basis in ritual and the language of story, a right-brain language that holds potent meaning for the subconscious. It would have actually diminished the healing effectiveness of Courtney's story, for instance, to try to make explicit the relationship between her dream and her history. A relationship undoubtedly existed, but allowing it to remain embedded in the events and symbolism of the dream gave Courtney's emotional processing a different and possibly more powerful effect than a discussion of feelings or facts.

Often the children's stories brought us face-to-face with the tragedy. Meg asked us to perform for her class one day. The children were attentive and ready. Most of them had been to shows in the gym and knew what to expect. Nine-year-old Don got up to tell the third story. He came right to the point.

"This is about my uncle Hakim. He got murdered. It was about three weeks ago."

We were instantly on guard. A story like this could spark a wildfire: too many of the children had had close contact with violent death and were ill-equipped to contain their feelings about it. We knew all too well what could happen if strong emotions were ignited. At the same time, we were ready to accept his story, to hold it and reflect whatever was most essential about it for him. We knew that telling such stories came from a drive for integration, an instinctive knowledge that bearing public witness to tragedy was one way to encompass it.

"My mom called to tell me, and then Bob had to take me to the city to go to the wake." The other children listened, riveted. The adults held their breath.

As Don told his story, Roselle in the audience turned her back, then left the room in tears. Warren, the assistant teacher, went after her. A few minutes later they returned. Warren sat close to her, sheltering her. Later Meg told me Roselle's appalling story: two years before, she had witnessed the murder of her baby brother by her stepfather.

We acted out Don's story, trying to show him what he wanted to see without overwhelming him and the others. Don watched quietly. But when the enactment was over he too leapt up and ran from the room, followed by Meg. By now most of the children were visibly upset, as were the Playback actors and the teachers. Disaster loomed. In another minute the entire group would be in crisis.

"Let's pull our chairs into a circle," I said, reaching for the guitar. "If you want to, you could cuddle up with one of the grown-ups." They all did. I sang:

When you see me looking sad
When you know I'm feeling bad
Put your arm around my shoulder
Hold my hand.

Some of the children cried. The adults comforted them, dabbing their own eyes. The tension began to ease. Don had come back in with Meg and was sitting nestled into her shoulder.

We sang another song with the children filling in the lyrics, then a goodbye song. The Playback team left.

An hour later I ran into Warren.

"Thought you'd like to know that Don and I have been talking. He says he's mad at his uncle because he never played with him enough and now he never will. The uncle was only about twenty, more like a big brother. Meg and I have been waiting for him to open up about it."

I was grateful for Warren's attitude to what had happened, his understanding that the near-breakdown in the classroom did not invalidate the healing that could come from the telling of a story like Don's. It was what I most wanted, this kind of working together for the children's benefit. Often, though, this goal seemed almost hopelessly out of reach, with my constant struggle to defend my work against skepticism—and sometimes against my own misgivings about its feasibility and effectiveness.

I often felt my heart seared by the pain endured by the children. Like most of the staff, I was tormented by the apparent impossibility of protecting them from harm. It seemed all the more important to offer Playback's redressive stage where suffering can be told and heard, its heavy burden lightened when shared.

Seven

GASTONIA

Billy Gaston was ten years old when I began seeing him. He'd already been at St Mary's for two years. He was tall for his age, affable and fidgety. He looked—and sang—rather like a junior Ray Charles. At that stage he was still an engaging and likeable child, in spite of a distinct oddness, but as he grew older his eccentricities grew worse in ways that were increasingly disturbing and distasteful to others.

Billy's unusual musicality emerged quickly and continued to develop steadily. In the beginning I saw him with a series of partners who came and went while Billy remained enthusiastic and engaged. Everything we tried—singing, composing, playing instruments—was a source of delight for him, an encounter with the radical and marvelous possibility that perhaps, after all, there was something in him that was gifted and well. I knew that clinically he was considered to be extremely disturbed. But in our sessions he was eager, courteous, and competent, if occasionally eccentric or glum.

After a year I stopped trying to match Billy with a partner for music sessions. The few other kids whose musical ability approached his were not emotionally ready to work with another child. And Billy, although apparently glad enough to have company in his sessions, was already acquiring the unpopularity which was to grow worse throughout his time at St Mary's. Other kids preferred not to spend time with him.

I began teaching Billy to play the recorder after a session in which he was uncharacteristically bad-tempered. It turned out that he had his heart set on learning the piano, not available to us in those earlier sessions in the cottage. "But you could learn to play the recorder," I said, getting one out of the cupboard and playing a tune for him. "Show me!" he said, intrigued. He surprised me with his aptitude. Several other children were learning to play but none as well as or as quickly as Billy. He practiced in his living unit, as much as he could amid the general mayhem and his own erratic behavior. One day he came in with a little tune he had composed, a sweet and mournful air in D minor.

"Billy, that's great! What a composer you are!"

"Me? I'm a jerk."

It never worked, I learned, to compliment him directly. His sense of himself as a walking disaster of a person was so entrenched that praise only made him anxious. But in his playing there was no tentativeness, no self-disparagement. His music embodied expansiveness whether he was trading inventive, graceful phrases with me on the resonator bells or improvising blues songs about whatever was on his mind.

In the springtime I heard about a choral concert that was to take place not far from St Mary's, involving children from a number of local elementary schools. I asked permission to take Billy and two other children to the concert, because of their special interest in singing. When I arrived in the early evening Billy was waiting in the living room, neatly dressed with a bow tie. But he seemed agitated as we walked out to the car.

"Calm down, Billy," said 11-year-old Kenia, herself perfectly poised.

"Sit in front with me," I said. He climbed in, muttering under his breath. As we turned onto the busy main street he opened the car door and leaned out. "Billy!" I yelled, slamming on the brakes.

"OK, OK, I'm sorry, just keep going, Jo," he said.

"Are you sure you want to go?"

"Yes, I really do."

With misgivings I drove to the concert, one eye anxiously on Billy. I stayed close to him as we found seats, high up on rickety bleachers in a huge gym. There were hundreds of people there, families of the performers. Billy looked around him wildly. As the concert began he mumbled something and began pushing his way back down to the floor. Kenia and Denyse rolled their eyes in exasperation. "Stay here," I told the girls. I climbed down the bleachers after him, ignoring disapproving looks from all the parents surrounding us. The choir launched into their patriotic opening number. Billy darted across the stage area and disappeared. Panicking, I followed just in time to see him duck into the boys' bathroom. I waited, hoping he'd emerge before I had to go in after him. A man appeared.

"I have a kid in there—could you check on him to see if he's OK?" I begged.

He looked reluctant but went in, coming out a moment later. "The black kid? He's throwing up."

Billy appeared after a few minutes, his anxiety now in full flower, twitching, incoherent, plucking at his clothes, then dashing back into the bathroom to vomit again. I didn't think I could leave him long enough to go back and get the girls. We stood in the lobby, listening to the massed voices inside. "Wow, they're good, aren't they?" said Billy. He sang along, faking the words, stepping restlessly from foot to foot.

At intermission, with Billy firmly by the hand, I went back into the gym and waved to the girls to come down. They were relieved to see us. Driving back to St Mary's, Billy was beside himself, threatening again to open the door and jump out. In desperation I began singing. Kenia and Denyse joined in. We sang the songs that Billy knew, the fishing song, the gospel tunes. To my intense relief, he began to sing with us. It calmed him. I didn't pause for breath until we drove into the St Mary's grounds. Billy was out of the car and into the building before I'd even opened my door.

Three days later in our next session we talked about what had happened. He was his usual friendly and thoughtful self with not a trace of Saturday night's panic. "I was acting crazy, wasn't I?" "Why, Billy?" "I don't know." He made up a song about the concert:

Well we went to a concert, me and the girls and Jo
I really wanted to be there, I really wanted to go
The kids they were good singers, I wish that I could too
I threw up in the bathroom, then we came back home.

I had learned through this ill-judged outing the extent of Billy's illness. There was a disjuncture, puzzling and persistent, between his relative sanity in music therapy sessions and his manifest craziness almost everywhere else. It was a disparity that grew more pronounced over the years that I knew him.

Billy continued in music therapy until his discharge at age thirteen, ending five years at St Mary's. Like Lizzie, he was discharged to a mental hospital: one of our failures. His final year was marked by escalating crises and a series of psychiatric hospitalizations. He was reviled by staff and children alike, thanks not only to his violent outbreaks but also to his egregiously bizarre and disgusting behavior. He had a tic of touching his genitals then smelling his hands. He accosted other children as well as female staff and even strangers on the street with aggressive sexual overtures. He ate out of the garbage. He sometimes spoke to people who were not there. He made animal noises all day, grunts, howls, squawks. In music therapy sessions he was a different person, a musician with by now considerable skills in composition, improvisation, and performance, always well-behaved, always fully engaged with his music. For ten months of this last year he came for sessions twice a week: the remarkable contrast in his demeanor, his very sense of himself, was consistent and sustained over time.

Billy spent a good deal of time creating and developing original compositions, blues that he would wail as though he'd been born in the Mississippi Delta, fragmentary love songs full of yearning and resignation, sometimes songs with ambitious instrumental settings. Drawing on innate musical sense rather than technique, he was able to play the synthesizer, piano, and drums convincingly. One piece he named "Gastonia," after himself, a rare mark of pride. At that time I had a music therapy intern, Wyatt, who came to one of Billy's sessions each week. Billy developed an arrangement for "Gastonia" that involved all three of us in a complex and artistic sequence using synthesizer, electric guitar, drums, violin and voice. The lyrics began with a reference to a habit of Billy's that was currently earning him much annoyance in the institution:

When you act like a dog you prove you're a dog
When you act like an animal you show it
When you act like a bird you fly like a bird
When you cry like a baby, you know it

Cry, baby, cry
Cry, baby, cry

Billy closed his eyes and dived deep into the chorus, his voice plaintive and urgent as he improvised on the keyboard over the chords that Wyatt played. We practiced the song for weeks and finally recorded it. "You're a maestro!" said Wyatt.

Billy made a list of other topics he'd like to write songs about: the Lord, poor people, loving and caring, church, Christmas, dancing and singing, good dreams, happiness, Easter. We were still working through the list when he left St Mary's for good, walking stiffly out the front door in his too-small suit, his dark face ashen.

Billy's concentration and the depth of his musicality were such that sometimes as we played I forgot for a moment that I was the therapist, he the seriously disturbed client. It felt like being with another musician, mutually absorbed in the kaleidoscope of melody, harmony, and rhythm. When we weren't actually playing, his oddity was clearly apparent—though it still seemed oddity rather than insanity. He spoke earnestly to his fingers when I challenged him to control his compulsive crotch-touching. He was endlessly puzzled by gender differences. "Is a girl's voice different from a boy's voice? Can you tell if it's a girl or a boy if you don't look?" Once, depressed, he sat at the synthesizer with his eyes closed, playing a slow single-note melody.

"Jo," he said without turning around, "I think I'm really dead."

"How can you tell, Billy?"

"Because of this music I'm playing."

Billy often chose to play the broken-down old piano, finding his way around the pattern of black and white notes and forgiving its many defects. I was fond of it too though frustrated by missing keys and non-functioning pedals. One day I got a phone call: Sister Christine, the executive director of St Mary's, wanted to talk to me. I was astonished. I had seldom spoken to her, and in fact she was rarely seen outside of the executive suites. "Tell her I can see her any time," I told her secretary, expecting a summons up to her elegant third floor office. "Are you free now?" said Frieda. "She'd like to come down to your room."

I hung up the phone and whipped around the Space Room with

the little carpet sweeper I'd bought to supplement the erratic job done by the cleaning staff. Sister Christine appeared at the door, tired-looking and somber in her nun's habit.

"I heard about your work down here," she said, looking around curiously. She reminded me of the Queen, remote and vulnerable at the same time. Her gaze stopped at the old piano with its broken panels and discolored keys. "Tell me what you do with the children." I described to her some of what went on in the Space Room; how the children took to music and found in it a language that spoke for them; how they wrote songs or composed instrumental pieces; how I saw the strengthening of self-esteem, the poignant expression of feelings too elusive for spoken words. Sister Christine listened, then cut me off. "I have to go back to my office in a minute." I was still mystified as to the reason for her visit. "I have some money I could put toward some instruments. Is there anything you need? I thought perhaps a new piano…" She trailed off. I was speechless.

"That would be wonderful!" I said, suddenly finding my tongue.

"Write me a budget." She named the amount she had at her disposal. It seemed prodigious to me. I thanked her warmly. She turned toward the door, then turned back.

"I used to love going to concerts when I lived in the city," she said. For another fifteen minutes she talked about the cultural richness that she missed now that she'd moved upstate, about orchestras and recitals and chamber music. She recommended a contemporary English composer whom I didn't know and wondered if the children might be able to sing his choral works.

"I must go," she said at last, smiling faintly. "Be sure and tell me what you'd like to get."

So it was thanks to Sister Christine that soon the Space Room had an immaculate, almost-new piano, as well as two huge rosewood chime bars with sonorous deep voices. Billy was thrilled, though briefly sad when the old piano was ignominiously hauled away.

In the treatment team meetings I found it difficult to talk about Billy's music. Sitting at the long table in the staff library, Jason, Billy's clinical coordinator, would lead us through the treatment plan, checking on his progress in relation to each stated goal. The staff had nothing but failure to report. They believed that Billy was beyond help or redemption. I would listen unhappily, waiting for my turn. I wanted very much for them to know about Billy's extraordinary progress in music. It wasn't just that he was talented, it was the consistent appearance of a different self that emerged when he was in the Space Room. The Billy I knew, vulnerable, cogent, expressive, creative, neither psychotic nor violent nor sexually aggressive, was as real as the monster they despised. I suspected that in fact the only way we as a treatment team could help him was to create a conspiracy of support for his musician-self, the organized, loving, creative aspect of his personality. Once I'd happened to pass him on the playing field and saw him seething with anger at another child, about to attack. I'd whispered to him "Is this the maestro?" Startled, he'd grinned and relaxed, remembering his other self, the Billy who was competent and strong. The fight was averted. But most of the time I wasn't around when trouble broke out, and I couldn't convince anyone else that the effort was worth it.

We finally got to the last page of the treatment plan where the goals for music therapy were listed. I started to talk about "Gastonia," about how Billy spoke and sang freely of love and depression and anger, about how his tic became manageable because I made sure, with his co-operation, that his hands were nearly always occupied, about his respectful and warm relationship with me, about how he had maintained his equanimity even when it had been tested by having another child join one of his weekly sessions.

But no one wanted to listen. The few allies I had in retaining sympathy for Billy were absent that day. The others chatted to each other about lunch, about the weather, about anything but Billy. I felt defeated.

Later I thought more about the staff's open hostility toward Billy and their conviction that he did not deserve respect or kindness. It was much easier for me, seeing him alone and at his healthiest, to maintain compassion for Billy, even knowing the ugliness of his behavior outside of music sessions. I didn't know how I might feel if my experience of him was as exclusively negative as it was for other staff.

My own goodwill and resilience were severely tested by George, a younger boy from the Anthonites, who, like Billy, was actively disliked by many of the staff as well as the children. George was a solidly-built African-American boy with an open expression that could change in a flash into a look of calculated wickedness. He enjoyed the singing sessions in the living unit but often his famously bad behavior asserted itself and he would have to be removed. He had a remarkable capacity to be disgusting—farting, spitting, smearing any body secretions he could get his hands on, all the while laughing a laugh that was unnervingly sinister for a nine-year-old. "Obnoxious" was most people's word for George, and they meant his foul mouth and flaring violence as well.

George asked me to take him for individual music sessions. He seemed earnest in these requests, and once I was convinced of his motivation I arranged to see him each week. Usually children were referred by clinical or teaching staff, but sometimes they referred themselves. If their requests seemed sincere enough, I'd consult with the treatment team and add the child to my schedule when I had an opening. "Be careful, Jo," said Marilyn. "If he gets upset he could hurt you."

But our sessions went well, on the whole, with lapses into provocation followed immediately by penitent good behavior. George was indeed delighted to have this chance to explore music. He learned to play simple tunes on the resonator bells, and began to compose his own. I was astonished at his musicality and his concentration. He would spend session after session practicing and developing compositions, which, though simple, were musical and aesthetic, to my ear. They pleased and surprised him as well.

I had learned by then to resist the naïve assumption that musicality like George's—or Billy's—somehow redeemed anti-social behavior. Many of us, especially artists of any kind, feel instinctively that artistic expression is inherently benign. We know from our own experience that our art connects us with the best in ourselves—that within it we are at our most expansive and inspired. We have to remind ourselves that, divine as art itself may be, artists don't necessarily allow this experience to guide their behavior as human beings. There were Nazis who played Schubert like angels. The significance of George's talent was simply that his music was, potentially, an important arena for growth. In it he might be able to find satisfaction, self-expression, connection, and meaning that would strengthen his mastery over impulsive violence.

One day he came in uncharacteristically subdued and close to tears. I knew what was on his mind. The previous morning he had attacked one of the childcare workers, punching her hard in the stomach and then in the face. He was a heavy boy, big enough to put considerable weight behind his blows. Bruised and shocked, Vanessa had been sent home.

"I feel so sad about Vanessa," he said. A tear rolled down his face.

"Why did you hit her, George?"

"I just got mad. I wish I didn't. I can't say sorry to her because she's still at home."

He dictated a letter to Vanessa, a remorseful and loving letter which he decorated with a picture of a person lying down in what looked like a flower garden. It took him almost the whole session. "Next time I want to make up a song for Vanessa."

George remembered his intention the next session but he couldn't find words for a song, instead composing another tune, this time a rather haunting and lovely melody over a chord progression that I played on the guitar. He looked at me as we found the ending, a disbelieving grin on his face. He was speechless with delight, the satisfaction of the creator who has found form for his vision. "Can we do it again?" he said after a minute.

We repeated it several times at his insistence. Each time George refined it slightly, making improvements in the phrasing and overall shape of it. There was no question that this was an artist at work.

As we left the Anthonite unit for his next session George saw Sean and remembered a squabble they'd had earlier in the day. "Suck my dick, Glass-eye," he sneered at Sean. Sean, painfully self-conscious about his eye, flew at him in a rage. Ted and Rita ran to help me pull the boys apart. George settled his clothes, calm in spite of the havoc he had just created. Sean struggled and fought in the arms of the childcare workers. As we left they had him pinned on the floor, sobbing into the grubby carpet. George listened soberly to my scolding as we walked to the cottage. By the time we got there he was full of regret. "Jo, I want to write an apology to Sean." I had misgivings. I didn't want him to think that his cruelty could be so easily atoned for.

George came to our first Playback Theatre show and loved it. "Are those people going to come back again?" he wanted to know. "Will you do my story if you do a show again?"

He told me the story. It was about his father who beat his mother and himself. "I was so scared, I hid in the closet when he hurt my mom. She was crying. One time the police came and I thought they were going to put me in jail." George looked very sad as he remembered this. "Then my dad went away and I got into trouble because I hurt my little brother, and I came here."

He wanted to make up music about this story, and with fierce concentration improvised several minutes of music, vividly expressive of violence, fear, and sorrow. I listened, a witness. He paused when he'd finished, then looked up with a question in his eyes.

"I could really hear it, George," I said.

He nodded, pleased. "But now I want to act it out. Can I?"

He wanted me to play his mother while he played both himself and his father. We acted out the scenes of the enraged man, the weeping woman, the frightened boy. When we'd finished George was tired but very calm.

Next session he wanted to enact the story again. This time we varied the roles, with George now playing his mother and I his father and himself. As his mother he seemed desperate, trapped. "Don't hurt my children!" he cried. But again at the end he was clear and calm, as if purged. "I miss my mom," he said with a sigh. I knew that she was still an involved and committed parent, in spite of George's unmanageable violence toward his brother and sometimes herself after her husband had left.

For weeks George spent part of every session exploring this story of physical rage and fear, his core story. I trusted his need to revisit it repeatedly, hoping that eventually these enactments and explorations would allow him to make his peace with an experience that had hurt and frightened him so badly—and might lead to a lessening of his own tendency toward violence. At one point I asked him if he'd like to make up a different ending for the story. George was thoughtful.

"OK. This time my mom is going to get him to stop hurting us, and then he's going to go away and never come back."

We acted this out. George seemed pleased, but not finished.

"I want to do it again, and *I'm* going to stop my dad this time." He had realized something important: worst of all for him had been his powerlessness to help his mother or himself. Now he re-lived the moment, this time with the will and strength to prevail over the father's brutality. Afterwards he was peaceful and satisfied.

George arrived at a later session stirred up after a home visit. He told me that his mother had lost her temper at his younger brother, forcing Tabasco sauce into his mouth to punish him for saying "fuck you." He wanted to act it out, but almost lost himself in impatient anger as we got ready. Re-visiting it in action calmed him. He ended the session playing serene music on the resonator bells.

He became angry again the following week when I asked him why he'd been confined to campus over the weekend, a punishment usually reserved for violence or running away.

"Shut up!" he shouted. "It's my business if I hit people!"

The next week George seemed depressed as we walked downstairs from his classroom. Eventually he told me that he'd been in a fight in school. Burdened by his sadness, he only wanted to listen to songs. "Sing that one, you know, 'Mean and Ugly.'" He listened with his head down. "That's just how I felt today."

"How do you feel now?"

"I want to cry," he said, but he didn't cry. He asked me to "Sing 'Over the Rainbow." By the end of the song he was asleep. Walking back to class he held my hand, something he hadn't done before.

A few minutes into his next session he began picking his nose, watching me to see how I would react. I handed him a tissue. He giggled, his signature unnerving laugh, and exaggerated the nose-digging, smearing his findings on the cushions. I warned him to stop. But he only laughed uproariously. He was in the grip of something and I didn't know how to reach him. I ended the session. He was taken aback. On the way back to his class he briefly threatened to run away or to pull the fire alarm, then thought the better of it.

"I just acted like that because I didn't want to come with you," he explained.

"You could have just told me, George."

In the Space Room the next week we discussed whether he could behave better than last time. He was eager to try. He picked up a puppet, a furry blue female character, and began to make up a story about her. She was a violent little girl, new to the group. She beat up all the other puppets. George put another puppet on his other hand. "I'm the childcare worker," he said, waving the second puppet. He told the little blue girl to talk to him when she was mad, instead of hitting. She needed to be told many times. Then she wept. "I'm really sad," she sobbed. She asked for some songs to sing, clapping along with "Oh Susannah," then dancing slowly and gracefully to "Over the Rainbow."

He put away the puppets, then asked to play his "Vanessa" tune. But as I handed him the mallets for the bells his mood changed abruptly. He threw them at me, laughing, then tried to hit me when I wouldn't let him grab them back. "I hate you, bitch," he yelled, no longer laughing as I gripped his wrists to stop him swinging at me. It took all my strength. George was almost as tall as me, and heavier. I yelled for Nolan, next door in the rec office. He came immediately. George, outnumbered, settled down quickly.

"I'm sorry, Jo, I didn't mean to, I'm sorry." He tried to hug me.

"Why did you get so mad, George?" I asked. But he couldn't tell me.

I thanked Nolan after the session, ashamed of my need for help. I was worried and puzzled, too. I'd hoped that George's violent impulses might have been tempered by all the work he'd done with the story about his father as well as by the repeated opportunity to express his creativity and tenderness in music. His scenario with the two puppets showed his own yearning to manage his anger better. And there was also the affectionate trust that was by now well-established between us. I wanted very much not to fail with George.

Next session George immediately apologized about last week. "Did you cry?" he asked me.

"No, but I didn't feel very good."

"I cried," he said.

George's angry outbursts were becoming increasingly frequent, usually beginning with giggling at his own grossness, then turning quickly to violence. I never knew when something would set him off or how far his anger would go before repentance took over. I was worried, both for George and for myself. I talked about him with the treatment team. The reports from all directions were similar: he'd recently been barred from home visits by his mother after one attack too many. "Look, we've tried just about everything and nothing makes a difference," said the psychiatrist. "At least he seems to have a connection with you." It was true, but it meant little when his mood took over.

I picked George up from his classroom for another session, pleased to find him calm and communicative. We improvised together on the resonator bells. George's playing was attuned, creative, imaginative. Then he farted. Immediately he snickered with glee, his round face distorted by an ugly leer. He was sinking fast. "Come on, George, let's keep playing," I said, but it was no use. He wanted only to wallow in his strange pleasure.

"OK, we have to stop, then."

He rushed at me, kicking and punching, picking up the wood and metal resonator bells and throwing them at me. I ran into the empty office next door, reaching for the phone to call for help. George was right behind me. He snatched the receiver out of my hand and slammed it with all his force into the side of my head. I grabbed the desk to keep from falling. Half-dazed, tears stinging my eyes, I got him upstairs to Mike Murray's office. George must have been already in his regret phase to let me lead him there, but I was beyond noticing.

It had been more than twenty years since anyone had hit me, but every cell in my body remembered the onslaught of pain, the sense of humiliation and injustice, the impossibility of retaliation, the desire to disappear from the face of the earth. Leaving Mike to deal with George, I got my coat and clambered down to the stream, crouching by the half-frozen water until the cold quiet soothed me and brought me back to myself.

I waited a couple of weeks before seeing George again. In the group singing sessions he was excessively affectionate and co-operative. I went to see him after school one day.

"George, you really hurt me. I need an apology before we can do music again."

He hung his head. "I'm very sorry, Jo," he said in a small voice. "I didn't mean to."

His words were heartfelt but I knew that his current remorse would not modify his violence next time he got angry at me. He wanted to keep coming for music therapy, a sign that in spite of what had happened it was still a source of something valuable for him. I told him that we'd keep going, but I was going to arrange for another adult to be there with us. He nodded, miserable and ashamed. I felt as bad as he did, discouraged that in the end I was unable to manage him alone. I was discouraged, too, by the evident failure of our work together to turn him away from violence.

George and Billy had in common both their unusual talent and the degree to which they aroused the dislike of the St Mary's community. For both boys, expressing themselves and building connection through music held at least the possibility of mastering some of the troubled emotion and behavior which were so problematic for them and for others around them. Billy, more disturbed as well as more gifted than George, was able over time to strengthen those aspects of himself which were healthy, creative, and joyful—to experience himself as successful in his musical endeavors and in his relationship not only with me but also with the music therapy intern, and later the other child who joined his Tuesday sessions. He remained, though, a severely mentally ill child, and even the full support from the rest of the staff, had I been able to get it, might not have changed the course of his illness.

Billy's and George's musical gifts neither cancelled out nor cured their pathology. But, to some degree, music released in each of these boys the capacity—unfamiliar and delightful to them—to create, to relate to others, to express vision and soul.

Eight

A PAINTING OF THE WORLD

Times were changing at St Mary's. I had been there for several years and my program was securely established. Some of the staff still viewed it, and me, with misgivings. I knew, from comments made directly to me as well as those I heard on the grapevine, that some people felt the arts had no place in treatment—that children as troubled as these needed a stricter, narrower approach. It was hard for them to trust that in the more spacious realm of artistic expression there still could be, and were, firm boundaries and clear goals. But many others had come to recognize that the children were benefiting from the regular opportunity to make music and to express themselves in drama. I felt part of a network of allies spread throughout the institution, from administration to maintenance.

The increasing acceptance of music and drama therapy bore fruit in other ways when grant money was found to launch a creative arts therapies program under the umbrella of the recreation department. With an art therapist and a dance therapist joining the staff, as well as a fluctuating crew of musicians, artists, writers, and craftspeople, there was a climate change at St Mary's. The majority of the children became involved in one or more of the arts. The basement domain of the rec department was transformed into a beehive of artistic activity. Art exhibits and murals appeared on the walls; a rock band rehearsed in the Space Room under the guidance of one of the young musicians; a student journal of "eco-poetics" published passionate verse and enigmatic drawings, edited by a bona fide beret-wearing poet.

With Nolan, who had a theatre background, I started a drama group with four children with the idea that we could use theatre games to develop imagination and expressiveness and help them work creatively as a team. If all went well we might help them develop a piece that they could perform. We discussed using Playback Theatre with them, but were concerned that it would be too challenging, and our brief attempts were not successful. It wasn't until later that I discovered how accessible and powerful Playback in fact could be as a group activity.

Consulting with the treatment teams, we invited kids who'd expressed an interest in drama, and who seemed emotionally ready to be in a group. There was Kenia, petite and self-possessed with a neat ponytail; shy, somber-eyed Julio; Leroy, a tall trickster with a basketball player's ambling gait; and Crystal, a roundish 12-year-old, pasty-skinned and asthmatic with big glasses perched on a snub nose. The four of them happened to represent the ethnic mix, if not the ethnic imbalance, of St Mary's: Latino Julio, Leroy the African-American, Kenia who was some combination of the two, and lily-white Crystal. (African-American and Hispanic children far outnumbered the white children at St Mary's: a disproportion so troubling in its implications of social injustice that no one ever commented on it.)

The first meeting began inauspiciously. I couldn't find Nolan for our planned briefing before picking up the kids. Annoyed, I rushed to Julio's class only to find that they were getting ready to go outside for an unscheduled dip in the pool. "Oh no," he said when he saw me, torn between two things he wanted to do. "Go with Jo, Julio," said Vicky, his teacher. "You'll be in the pool after school anyway." He decided he'd come, to my relief. We found the others and headed down to the Space Room. Nolan appeared just as we were getting started, out of breath and apologetic after a sprint from the parking lot.

We talked to the kids about drama and what we thought we'd do in this group.

"I thought we were going to be doing a play," said Kenia, disappointed.

"Give it a try," I suggested. "Maybe it will be as much fun as a play." She pouted.

"I don't care, I don't like learning lines," said Crystal. She and I had done some one-on-one music therapy together that had quickly broadened to poetry-writing and painting as well. Crystal was one of the most talented people I'd ever met in my life.

We showed them how to do Mirrors. Face to face with a partner, one person follows the other's every movement and facial expression as if she were a mirror. I watched Leroy trying to trick Julio with sudden movements. "See if you can move so slowly that I can't tell who's leading," I said. Immediately they united in trying to fool me instead of each other.

In spite of the children's genuine eagerness to act, it was hard for them to learn to work together. Small irritations impeded every step. The mercurial politics of school and group life came right into the Space Room with us. Kenia and Leroy struck up a flirtation that was much more engrossing for them than anything Nolan and I had to offer. Seeing Leroy through Kenia's eyes, Crystal began to find him attractive too, which she expressed by needling him. I found myself getting bossy. "Kenia! Leroy! Crystal! If you can't settle down and concentrate I'm going to ask you to go back to class."

Eventually, in desperation, Nolan and I set up a point system to try and improve the standard of behavior. Almost everything else in their day—classes, meals, after-school activities—offered opportunities to either gain or lose points. Earning points led to coveted rewards: extra privileges, a trip uptown to Floster's Department Store where a very small amount of money would get you a plastic devil mask or some Silly Putty. Losing points meant more restrictions, no pool, no free time, no Nintendo. The idea was that, according to the principles of behavior modification, these rewards and penalties would teach the children to behave better. The B-mod system at St Mary's operated in conjunction with other approaches and was not applied rigidly, and in some situations it did seem to help remind the children to refrain from aggression or to apply themselves in class. But my observation was that external rewards often in fact deflected a child's attention from a much deeper, inner satisfaction that came from their own achievement. As Alfie Kohn says in *Punished by Rewards*, "'Do this and you'll get that' automatically devalues the 'this.'"

Except for Crystal, who maintained philosophically that arts activities should be exempt, like therapy, the children accepted that the point system applied in drama group too. They were pleased when they got their point, cross and disappointed when they lost it. It didn't seem to influence their actual behavior at all. Nolan and I felt like hypocrites. Try as we might, we didn't believe in points.

Nolan and I met to talk about our original idea for a performance. I'd had second thoughts, realizing that the pressures of performing could easily outweigh any benefits of the work we were doing with the kids. I wasn't at all sure that performing, in general, was therapeutically justified for children whose ego strength was so tenuous. Using the performing arts in therapy, it was essential at every moment to keep the focus on the process, not the product. Even if Nolan and I ourselves were clear about the relative unimportance of the performance itself, we were worried that the children could be tripped up by anxiety, canceling out whatever they'd gained from the sessions themselves. On the other hand, we wanted to them to experience the sense of achievement that a successful performance can engender.

"How about if we did something on videotape?" Nolan suggested.

It seemed a good solution. We could film it without pressure of time or a live audience.

I wrote the skeleton of a play about a boy called Paul who had a secret. The play had an algorithmic structure in which the children could insert characters, ideas, and dialogue. They decided what Paul's secret was, who the other characters would be, the turns and outcome of the plot. All their suggestions came from their own lives, openly acknowledged by them in some instances, not in others. The play gave them a chance to explore personal concerns without having to reveal more than they wanted to.

Once we'd created the story, the children practiced it scene by scene, serious now with the focus of refining the play. They developed dialogue, remembering and repeating the lines they liked, though nothing was written. Their acting was natural and convincing. They seemed to share a sense of responsibility for the story, cueing each other when necessary while staying in role.

I realized after a couple of weeks that our carefully-designed point system had fallen by the wayside. The children had not noticed or complained, by now amply motivated and rewarded by what they were creating together.

The play opens with Paul, played by Julio, in class. Paul is looking very gloomy. His friend Robin (Kenia, confident and down-to-earth) tries to find out what's on his mind. He denies there's anything wrong.

"Don't forget about football after school," says Robin.

"Can't go," says Paul, gloomier than ever.

"You're not going to football? Paul, something's going on. Why can't you tell me? I'm your best friend in the whole school."

"All right, there is something. But it's my secret." Robin is about to argue but Ms Haynes (Crystal, whose matronly air made her everyone's choice for the role of the teacher) comes in and begins class.

In Scene Two, Robin and Vinnie are at lunch in the cafeteria, toying with some ugly-looking lasagna. (Leroy played Vinnie, and the real-life friendship between him and Kenia underlay their acting.)

"Vinnie, something's going on with Paul." says Robin. "He's got a problem, something serious."

"What do you think it could be?" says Vinnie

"I don't know, maybe his cat ate poison and died."

"Maybe his mom lost her job."

"Maybe his dad had to go back to prison."

"Maybe he got beat up."

"Maybe his brother was in a car accident."

"Maybe they're getting kicked out of their house."

"Maybe his dad wears ladies' clothes." They laugh, then become serious. "He's not going to football today. It must be really bad."

Just then Ms Haynes appears, flustered and upset. "Do either of you know anything about some money that's gone missing from my desk? It was for the field trip tomorrow. If it doesn't turn up we can't go."

Vinnie and Robin shrug. After she leaves, they look at each other.

"Maybe Paul took it. Maybe that's his secret."

Scene Three is in the school library. Paul is slouched over a book. Robin and Vinnie move their chairs closer and closer to him until he looks up, startled.

"Paul," says Vinnie. "Did you take the money for the field trip? Is that your secret? You should just give it back, man. Otherwise we can't go."

Paul is hurt and confused. "I didn't take no money. What are you talking about?"

Ms Haynes rushes into the library. "I found it!" she says. "I'd put it somewhere else and I forgot. What a relief!" She looks around and sees their faces. "What's going on, guys?"

Robin looks at Paul. "Vinnie and I, we're worried about Paul. He won't tell us what's wrong. We thought maybe he'd taken your money."

Ms Haynes sits down. "Why don't you tell us about it, Paul? It's awful to feel bad all alone."

Paul sighs. Then at last he tells his secret. "My mom took me to the hospital and they did all these tests. And they found out I have epilepsy."

The others are quiet.

"What's epil-epsy?" says Robin, stumbling over the word.

"It's when you blank out and fall down, and you don't remember," says Paul.

"I had bad asthma when I was your age, Paul," says Ms Haynes. "Sometimes I had to go to the hospital in an ambulance. I didn't want to tell anyone about it."

"I didn't want to tell anyone when my mom got fired," said Robin.

"I hate it when people know about my dad," said Vinnie.

The kids and Ms Haynes decide to go get an ice cream after school.

"Are you allowed to have ice cream, Paul?" said Ms Haynes.

"If it's a double scoop," he says, with a little grin.

We filmed the play on location around St Mary's, carefully maneuvering times when we could keep other people out of Vicky's classroom and the staff cafeteria. We chose a song to play on tape between scenes and behind the handwritten credits at the end:

Frost is in the air
Changes everywhere, darlin'
This time of year
A change comes over me

At the children's request we filmed a post-play scene in which Kenia introduced each member of the cast. They stood proudly together looking at the camera, arms around each other's shoulders.

We met for a final session and watched our film. The kids were thrilled, high-fiving each other at every dramatic or funny moment. We played a last drama game, standing in a circle and giving each other imaginary gifts. Leroy gave Julio a wheelbarrow full of bubblegum. Julio gave me a Rolls Royce, with keys. Kenia gave Leroy a Concorde. I gave Crystal a holly bush. Nolan gave Kenia a motor bike. Crystal gave Nolan a painting of the world.

Nine

THE BAG OF STONES

In the early stages of the drama group Nolan and I had experimented
with including Playback Theatre. It didn't work. Kenia, Crystal, Julio,
and Leroy found it hard to understand the format and preferred the
other activities we offered. But later, when Playback Theatre shows
became a regular feature at St Mary's, many of the children were eager
to act as well as tell. Sometimes we would invite one or two of them to
join us onstage in a minor role. But in general we knew it was too risky
to give these very volatile children the responsibility of enacting the
stories, at least in a performance context. On the other hand, I was
aware of the potential therapeutic benefits to be gained from the
experience of acting as well as telling in Playback: the chance to develop
expressiveness, empathy, connection to others, the satisfaction of
creating theatre, a sense of teamwork and belonging. I organized
therapy groups of four or five children in which they would take part
in workshop-model Playback Theatre, learning how to enact stories as
well as telling them in weekly 45-minute sessions. Each group met six
times.

I knew from the outset that I would need someone to lead with
me, for logistics—escorting children in different directions before and
after sessions; for occasional crisis management—a reasonable
likelihood with St Mary's population; and, most importantly, to support
and guide the children's acting while I conducted. Prue, one of the
members of the St Mary's Playback group and a school psychologist,
was willing to co-lead. In the initial phases of each group Prue played
whichever role required the most delicate handling, usually that of the
teller. As the groups gained cohesion and confidence, I would invite

the teller to choose freely from any of the actors. We made other adaptations as well, aimed at maximizing the children's success. We omitted music during the scenes since it was too difficult for them to create sensitive improvised music, nor was it practical to bring in another staff member. We also stopped using the fabric props when we saw that they were more distracting than helpful. As the conductor I gave far more direction to the actors than I would for adults, including, sometimes, a brief narration to begin the story, to move it along in the middle if it got stuck, or to cue an ending. We routinely debriefed with sharing after stories so that actors as well as tellers could speak about their experience during the enactment.

Each session followed a similar sequence, creating a sense of familiarity and safety for the creativity and openness that we were invoking. The quality of ritual in the structure of each session echoed the framing of the enactments themselves. We began with a song of greeting as we sat on the circle of pillows, sometimes followed by another "fill-in" song in which each child could contribute a line expressing a feeling, an experience, or a wish. The warm-up phase also included, usually, one or two carefully-chosen drama games designed to develop expressiveness and connection. Such activities were structured to make them as accessible and enjoyable as possible. For example, in a game that required partners, we would pair the children with me and Prue until they were ready to work successfully with each other.

When it was time for stories, we would set up our "stage" with plastic milk crates along one wall for the actors, the piano bench on one side for teller and conductor, and the pillows moved back for the "audience." The children learned the simple Playback procedure of the enactment itself: the telling of the story, the standing of the actors as they are chosen, the "Let's watch!" injunction of the conductor to signal the beginning of the action, the pause at the end when the teller is acknowledged by the actors, and the conductor's invitation to the teller to make a final comment.

After one or two stories, we returned to the circle of pillows for several minutes of sharing—how was it for the teller, for the actors, for the children watching if there were any. The purpose was to express any feelings or memories that had been stirred, not to offer analysis or counsel. (Sharing was another adaptation, drawn from psychodrama — in non-clinical Playback Theatre, we do not pause to share after enactments, instead trusting in the natural dialogue between stories and in the capacity of performers and audience members to cope with their individual responses.) We ended with a goodbye song, again acknowledging each child by name.

This routine, of course, was liable to change shape as each session evolved. Sometimes a warm-up activity expanded to take up most of the session (like the role-playing activity described in chapter ten). At moments of particular intensity we might pause and return to the pillows for a song to help everyone express, contain, and integrate emotion. Singing became such a key element in these groups that the children sometimes initiated improvised songs, individually or as a group, as another way to tell their stories.

Sharelle had been in one of the Playback therapy groups for several weeks. In the fifth session she told about a memory from when she was two years old. Finding her playing alone outside on the porch, her stepfather had picked her up and dangled her over the railings, chuckling as she screamed in terror for her mother inside. The mother didn't come, either not hearing or not caring.

I asked Prue to play Sharelle's stepfather. Sharelle chose waif-like Aimee to play herself and Olly to be her mother. To my surprise, Olly agreed readily to this cross-gender role. He was a quiet boy, self-conscious about a bad stammer. They acted it out. I could see Olly struggling with the desire to come and help Aimee/Sharelle as she screamed in fear. But he stayed true to the story.

"Yeah," said Sharelle when they'd finished. "Felt like that."

Aimee and Olly looked pleased.

"It-it was weird b-being a m-mom," said Olly.

Watching the story was freckle-faced Herman, whose stocky frame brimmed with held-in violence. Herman had managed a surly containment in the four sessions of this group so far, though occasionally snapping at the two African-American children, Sharelle and Olly. "I wish the mom had come out and helped her," he said, his hands pressed to his throat as always when he spoke. "I felt bad for Sharelle." I hadn't heard this kind of expression of pity and identification from him before.

He wanted to tell the next story. It was the first time he'd offered to be a teller.

"See my T-shirt?" We looked at his grubby red T-shirt with the words "BORN TO BAKE" written on it in big letters. "I made a huge batch of cookies for my church. I had to stay up late to do it, because the guy who was going to do it got in an accident the day before the fair. So they gave me this T-shirt." Herman grinned, a rare warming. He chose Olly to play himself and Sharelle to play the woman who had the T-shirt made for him. Aimee played the chocolate-chip cookies.

Herman's brother Derek joined another of the Playback groups, in spite of warnings to us that he was even more violence-prone than his brother. Like Herman, Derek was broad and slow-moving, with a closed expression and hunched shoulders. Like his brother, too, he had an unusual air of thoughtfulness, along with an aura of menace. Derek interested me. In the first session I kept an eye on him, alert for signs of irritation that (we'd heard) could escalate fast. But he was withdrawn and impassive, shaking his head when we invited him to take part in warm-up games. He sat in the audience as the others acted out a story, pleasure crossing his face for the first time as he watched.

We sat on the pillows to talk about next week. Derek reached casually under his shirt and pulled out a small cloth bag threaded on a cord around his neck. The bag hung there unremarked upon by the others. Just as it was time to leave, he spoke up.

"Can I show you my special stones?"

I thought he might mean pebbles from the stream. "Sure," I said.

Derek unhooked the bag from his neck and poured its contents into his palm, holding it out so all could see. In his outstretched hand was a little pile of beauty: pieces of amethyst, turquoise, rose quartz, tiger's eye.

On Wednesdays we met with another group. One week there were only two children: most of the kids had left already for Easter home visits. Verity and William were pleased since such a small group meant that both of them would get a chance to tell stories.

Verity went first. A small, mannerly 12-year-old white girl with glasses and a blandly smiling face, Verity talked a great deal about heaven and hell and how she wanted to be a nun when she grew up. She was the adopted child of a minister and his wife, harsh people who had bent her will and distorted her soul with years of impossible demands and severe punishments. She was convinced beyond any doubt of her wickedness. I found her not wicked but strange. Once in the Lying Game, where everyone has to tell something that might or might not be true, she'd said, smilingly, "I killed my parakeet." Everyone held up crossed fingers to show their disbelief. "It's true," she'd said, and she told us how she had played beauty parlor with the parakeet, covering it with soap, spraying it with hairspray, then cutting its wings like hair. In another session when the children were expressing grief about the death of one of the kitchen workers, Verity had demurred. "I'm happy," she'd said, "because now I'll talk to him in heaven. I often talk to people in heaven to make them feel better."

Verity sat in the teller's chair and told her story. She was calm, articulate. "This happened on my home visit last week. I went to the mall with my parents. When we were in the car, my mom started telling me how my older sisters don't want to be with me any more, because they're too grown-up. Then when we were at the mall, she went into Sears and my dad got some popcorn and he told me that I wasn't going to live with them any more. I started crying, and he said 'Why are you crying, Verity?' But I didn't know how to explain."

Verity's customary pleasant expression stayed firmly in place as she told her story. Prue and I had heard earlier in the day about her parents' decision to reverse the adoption. Upset as I'd been in the meeting, it was more painful to hear her own bald account.

It was too much to ask William to play either Verity or the parents in this story. Instead I asked him to sit with Verity and keep her company as she watched. Verity chose Prue to play herself. I acted her mother, then her father the minister. As Verity, Prue cowered and whimpered as I announced that she couldn't stay with the family. "Oh, stop making such a fuss, Verity," I said as the father. "Now wait here while I see if your mother has finished her shopping."

As we acted her story Verity responded at first by giggling. But when we finished there were tears rolling down her cheeks. William held her hand and watched her with grave concern on his gentle, asymmetrical face. Verity's expression was still bland; there was no sobbing, just those steady tears. Prue and I hugged her. William came in close and I reached out to include him. We talked about how she deserved to have parents who loved her and who knew how lucky they were to have her. Verity was unconvinced. The belief that she was bad, that rejection was inevitable and earned, was etched into her bones.

I invited her to imagine, if she wanted to, being with a different kind of family. Slowly she began to describe a scene which took on detail and form as she spoke.

"OK, I'm at the park." She paused. "Yes, I'm at the park, and I'm with my mom, only she's a different mom, she's younger and she's nice. She's got short brown hair. We're in the swimming pool and she's teaching me how to swim." Verity smiled. "My big brother is there too. My mom gives him some money and he gets some snacks for us."

Prue, William, and I acted out the new scenario. We tried to make this image of warmth and belonging as vivid as the other, as if it could blot out that terrible inscription on her bones. Verity smiled and nodded with conviction at the end.

"I hope one day you find a family like that," said Prue.

"Can William tell a story now?" asked Verity. Last week William had told us about the first time he was taken away from his mother three years ago when he was seven "because she couldn't handle me." Now he wanted to tell about the second time, when he was placed in a children's psychiatric center for three months.

"William, think of either a good moment from that time or a bad one," I suggested. His memory had been jogged by Verity's fantasy story: he told about learning to swim with Margaret, the kind-hearted lifeguard. Verity played Margaret with enthusiasm, her own story at rest for the moment.

"Come on, William! Kick those legs! You don't want to sink, do you? Then I'd have to rescue you!"

Both the children laughed, a free and childlike sound.

Group therapy of any kind at St Mary's was rare because of the children's instability: we were prepared for our experiment to fail as many others had. But it didn't. The children relished the opportunity to tell stories in a more intimate setting. As in the performances, their stories often told of normality and humor, hope and love. But the intimacy and continuity of the group also allowed them to tell more tender stories, stories of loss or vulnerability that could be told only to trusted listeners (though still avoiding the stories of their worst traumas, sensing that even the relative safety of these groups was not enough to hold the extreme disclosures that many of them could have made). Though in most cases not especially talented, the children were generally able to bring enough accuracy and sensitivity to their enactments to satisfy the teller, watching his or her story from a light trance induced by telling it. The teller's trance—the special state of mind and imagination that allows tellers to *see* the characters and location of their story as it's enacted—often allows tellers to be fully satisfied even when the actors have done a mediocre job. (Audience members, on the other hand, are not as readily entranced, so Playback Theatre in a performance setting requires a much higher level of skill on the part of the actors.)

The children responded gleefully to the acting games and songs, often using them to express feelings in somewhat oblique and therefore unthreatening form. We saw signs of a subtle impact on their sense of themselves as people, as citizens of St Mary's. Day and night the message of their environment was that they were burdens, misfits, the cause of trouble for everyone around them—"emotionally disturbed." As actors in each other's stories they found an unfamiliar and significant opportunity to be the agents of comfort and learning for each other: helpers, not problem-causers.

Perhaps most significant of all was the growth of empathy. Their tolerance and understanding toward each other grew with their willingness to take on roles that crossed racial and gender divides as well as the ever-fraught and complicated network of hostilities and allegiances. As they acted in or witnessed each others' stories, they found themselves stepping into another person's feelings in a way that they had seldom done before, like Herman's rare expression of concern and identification with the two-year old Sharelle, or African-American Lester's effective portrayal—after an initial refusal—of a white grandma. "She's just like that!" said the teller in surprise. "How did you know?" "Thought about my own grandma," responded Lester. Taking roles in each other's stories, witnessing and reflecting each other's experiences, engendered a compassionate fellow-feeling that was generally absent from the interactions of children who had had little chance to learn about empathy from the adults in their lives.

In spite of numerous chaotic moments and occasional crises, the groups more than met our expectations as well as those of the children. There were many revelations as precious and unexpected as Derek's hidden treasures. Most of the children expressed a wish to continue longer than the six weeks limit placed on us by the school authorities, understandably concerned about the children missing too much of their academic studies.

To a large degree it was the ritualistic structure, both the protocol of enacting a Playback scene, and the design of each session itself, which accounted for the success of these groups. We organized time and space so that the children felt not only safe, generally, but invited and honored. They instinctively recognized the age-old presence of ritual, of a frame in which their personal experiences could be communicated and held. Our circle of pillows on the floor, where we sat to greet each other and sing, embodied this framing of our time together, as did the setting up each session of the simple Playback "stage."

Playback Theatre is above all built around this sense of ceremony, the deliberate creation of an artistic and truth-telling space that is distinct from ordinary life. It is the element of ritual that accounts for Playback's power in any circumstance. The St Mary's children recognized and responded to it, telling their important stories to each other and enacting them with compassion, creativity, and respect.

We of course encountered difficulties as well as success. The most challenging aspect was building integration with the rest of the St Mary's program. I knew that a number of staff members appreciated the therapeutic value of the Playback Theatre performances. The attitude of these staff members—teachers, therapists, childcare workers—greatly enhanced the effectiveness of what we were doing. They took Playback seriously and made themselves available to follow up after a story that exposed a vulnerable experience, as Warren did after Don's story of his Uncle Hakim's murder. But some other staff found it hard to understand the point of Playback Theatre, seeing it either as entertainment or a subversive encouragement for the children to believe their own faulty versions of reality, as one critic put it. It had been, in part, to improve this situation that I had initiated the therapy groups. My hope was that inviting staff members to make referrals, and providing ongoing progress reports, would lead to an increased and synergistic understanding of the Playback approach, to the benefit of the children. There was indeed some improvement, and some of the teachers and other staff went out of their way to support the children's participation. But my vision of Playback Theatre as a fully integrated strand in the St Mary's tapestry of treatment was never fulfilled to the degree I'd hoped and felt was possible.

The other challenge was the precariousness of the children's interactions. The atmosphere at St Mary's was often heavy with violence. Many children were prone to losing control, at risk of hurting themselves, each other, or staff members. Although the ritual structure of Playback itself and of our sessions created a context of safety to a surprising degree, there were also occasions when one or more children had to be removed to avert conflict. We had to resort to a physical restraint once—only once—when a girl became hysterically giggly as she acted out a story and could not regain control, spiraling rapidly toward violence.

We learned that for children to succeed in Playback Theatre therapy they needed enough ego strength to step into another role without losing the awareness of their own identity: some of the younger children, especially, could not cope with acting out even brief moments or feelings told by other group members. The Playback groups were also not suitable for the few near-psychotic children at St Mary's. For a child who was unsure of the boundaries of reality, it was not safe to venture as an actor into the zone of "as if." But such fragile children could, and did, tell their stories successfully in the more distanced setting of the performance format.

Ten

CHRONICLES OF A PLAYBACK GROUP

Like a pair of Pied Pipers, Prue and I collected children from their various classrooms, our string growing as we progressed toward the Space Room for the first session of a new group. The children came in, curious and a little shy, and sat down on the circle of pillows. From staff referrals we'd chosen two girls and three boys: tall, quiet Elizabeth, pixie-ish Kiki, Malcolm, calm and mature-seeming, with a habit of ducking his head to avoid eye contact; Albert with red hair and a touch of rakish glamour about him, and Ronnie, small and messy with shirt hanging out and glasses held together with Scotch tape. Malcolm and Kiki were African-American, the others white. All were 12 or 13 except Kiki, a precocious 9-year-old. Ronnie looked and behaved much younger than his actual years.

Sitting on the pillows, we sang a song of greeting. The kids joined in, briefly self-conscious then relaxing into enjoyment.

Here we are, it's another day,
Just one thing that I would like to say,
Oh Kiki, and Albert, hello to you.

We sang around the circle, naming everyone.

I explained to them that in this group everyone was going to have a chance to tell stories and to act them out for each other. "And when you're not being an actor you can be a witness," I said. They looked at each other, confused.

"A witness?" asked Kiki. "You mean like in court?"

I realized this was the wrong term for children who were all too familiar with courtroom lingo. "I mean, you can be the audience. It's good to have someone to watch." They nodded.

"Is this therapy?" asked Elizabeth.

"Yes," said Prue. "We want it to be helpful to you. We want it to be fun too." They nodded again, accepting.

Malcolm volunteered to tell the first story, after we'd played a couple of warm-up games.

"When I was home last time," he began, "me and my cousin got into trouble because we took eggs from his mother's refrigerator and we threw them at kids in the street. So she got mad—she gets really mad sometimes but she don't hit us—and she made us go to the store and get some more eggs for her, with our own money. When we were in there, this kid, he was an older kid that my cousin knew, he told us to give him the eggs, but we wouldn't. So he waited for us outside the store, and he had a gun. So we gave him the eggs."

My head spinning from guns and eggs in the same breath, I asked Prue to play Malcolm and invited him to choose actors for the other parts. As the teller's actor, Prue would help keep the story on track.

They acted it out, Malcolm and I watching from the side. The kids surprised me by how well they remembered what their characters said and did. Albert played the bully with the gun. He managed to rein in his restless energy until the right moment, when he stepped into the scene with a menacing swagger. Malcolm was riveted.

"Yeah, that's what it was like," he said, shaking his head. "Man!" He was quiet for a moment. "Then later on, my other cousin, John, he really did get shot a couple of blocks from there. They killed him."

The other kids stared at him. Prue and I waited. Malcolm's eyes were far away.

"Malcolm?" I said after a minute. "Do you want to tell us more about that?"

He turned to me, back in the room again. "Nope."

We came back to the circle of cushions for the last ten minutes of the session. I invited the kids to tell us what Malcolm's story might have reminded them of in their own lives. "Or you could tell us what it felt like being an actor."

"My grandma was shot in the stomach," said Ronnie. He seemed more proud than upset.

"I got shot in the arm. Look." Albert pulled up his sleeve to show a scar. "My brother's friends were fooling around. They were trying to scare me and they sure did."

I couldn't get used to the dreadful familiarity so many of the children had with gun violence. For them it was evidently normal—unpleasant but not shocking.

I asked Albert what it was like to play the threatening teenager in Malcolm's story.

"I felt bad! That guy was ugly." I thanked him for doing it. I told them that it was a kind of a gift they could give each other, to play the tough roles in each other's stories.

"I got something to say," said Malcolm, who'd been listening without comment. "I hate guns. I hate people who use guns. They spoil everything for everyone. It's not fair." Malcolm was passionate. "My aunt, she belongs to Mothers Against Guns, and I think they're really cool. They want to make things safe again. They're sick of kids being killed."

It was time to go back to class. "Our plan is to meet every week for six weeks," I reminded them. "But it's your choice now. What do you think? Do you want to keep going?"

"Yes!" they all chorused. Prue and I looked at each other, pleased.

The children wanted to talk about Malcolm's story when we met again.

"It was a sad story," said Kiki, wrinkling her nose. "I don't really like sad stories."

"It wasn't so sad, though," said Elizabeth. "At least Malcolm didn't get shot."

"What I think is, if something bad happens, it's better to tell people about it. At least they get to know about it," said Albert.

"Yeah," said Malcolm. "Anyway my story wasn't that bad, not as bad as what happened to my other cousin." They were silent.

Later in the session Kiki had a story to tell. "I thought about this yesterday, that I would like to tell it when I came to the group. It's about when I was seven, and I was living with my mother and my little brother, Mason. He was four." Kiki, sweet and smart, had been removed from the dangerous care of her mother when she was eight. "My mom, she used drugs all the time, and her boyfriend too, and he used to beat her up when they got high." Once again I found myself trying to listen attentively while sickened inside by what I was hearing. "I was playing with my little brother in our room and I could hear them hunting everywhere for that thing that you use—you know, Malcolm, what's it called?" She mimed with her hands.

"You mean the cooker?"

"Yeah, that's it. Anyway, I was very scared because I had thrown it out the window. I knew they'd both beat me up if they found out. But then my mom told me to take Mason to the store. I sure was glad to get out of there."

The actors, Prue as Kiki, acted it out. Kiki snuggled in as close to me as she possibly could, gripping my arm tightly. "Yeah, that really did feel like my story," she said, letting her breath out at last when it was over.

The others talked about what it was like for them to play it. "Sad," was the comment of most of them. "I felt sad for Kiki," said Elizabeth.

"Kiki, did you think it was a sad story?" I asked her, remembering her comment about Malcolm's story.

"Yes, it was, but I'm still glad I told it."

We talked, and sang, and acted out one more story. But they were still stirred up. I showed them how to take deep breaths and let their bodies relax as they exhaled.

It was time to end. Kiki turned and hugged me. "Anyone else want a hug?" I asked. They all did.

Albert arrived in a strange mood, disheveled and hollow-eyed. "I'm on special alert," he announced to everyone. "I got restrained five times today. I'm not allowed to go home for more than three days over vacation." The 10-day Easter break was coming up. I hadn't heard what the special alert was about, but it was usually the result of suicide threats. I knew that the anguish in his family was more than enough to make a child question the value of living. Albert and his siblings had been abused for years by both their father and uncle. Now in puberty, he'd got into trouble himself for sexual threats to younger children. The father had recently died of AIDS. The children and their mother lived with the knowledge that they might be infected, though tests so far were negative.

I watched Albert for signs of depression, and to see if he wanted to use this chance to explore what was on his mind. He didn't, instead sabotaging the other children's attempts to express anything serious.

"I was thinking about something this week…" began Elizabeth.

"Hoo-wee! Elizabeth knows how to think!" interrupted Albert. "Make a note of that, will ya, Ronnie?" Ronnie was always ready to play along with Albert's clown, but their comedy act had never been as disruptive as it was today.

"Let's everybody take some deep breaths," suggested Malcolm at one point when tempers were rising. It helped, but only briefly. Prue and I finally gave Albert an ultimatum: settle down or go back to class. Albert saw that we meant it. His demeanor changed. "OK, I'll calm down. Don't send me back." He tried hard for the rest of the session, lapsing sometimes but then catching himself. Ronnie followed his cues precisely.

We asked the kids, one at a time, to enter the room in the role of someone they knew well—"Think of someone who really likes you" was my instruction. Elizabeth went first.

"I'm Mrs Tait, Elizabeth's mom," she announced, sitting down in a chair.

"Welcome to the Space Room, Mrs Tait. Please tell us about your daughter Elizabeth."

"Well, I think she's wonderful," said Elizabeth as her mother. She told us about Elizabeth's ambition to become a schoolteacher. "And she'd be a good teacher. She really likes little kids."

We thanked "Mrs Tait" and said goodbye. Malcolm went next. He came into the room with a ghetto walk and sat down in the chair with his arms folded and his legs splayed out.

"I'm Malcolm's cousin Gabe. Malcolm told you about me. We almost got shot when this kid wanted our eggs, remember?"

"Hi, Gabe. What can you tell us about Malcolm?"

"He's OK. We do everything together. We're like this." Malcolm held up his fingers firmly linked together. "I look out for him, he looks out for me."

"What do you like best about Malcolm?" asked Prue.

"Gabe" was suddenly bashful. "Well, it's like, it's just that he's my best friend, and my cousin too." He paused. "All I can say is, we stick together, and if one of us gets in trouble, we both get in trouble."

"So maybe you could help each other stay out of trouble, Gabe, what do you think?"

"Yeah, I guess."

We had time for one story. Ronnie told about getting sent to the crisis room during school the day before. For the first time in this group, I invited him to choose any actors he wanted. He chose Malcolm to play himself, Prue for the teacher, Albert for the easygoing crisis room supervisor who played cards with him. Malcolm did a fine job.

We played the Lying Game, one of their favorites. Ronnie said: "Me and Albert are brothers." Everyone except Albert held up two crossed fingers to show they didn't believe it. Ronnie and Albert protested in unison. "It's true!" For once they were not clowning.

"He's lived next door to me all my life," explained Albert. "We *are* like brothers."

"Yeah," said Ronnie. I'd never seen him so intense and serious.

We had discovered too that there was another connection that Prue and I had been unaware of when we chose children for this group: Kiki and Elizabeth had also known each other before coming to St Mary's. These long-established friendships accounted, at least to some extent, for some of the unusual cohesion of the group.

Albert was eager to continue the "interviews." I'd heard meanwhile from his therapist that he'd suggested this activity in their session. In the role of his friend Thomas, he'd talked about how upset Albert was about the fighting that went on at home, with four wild children and a helpless mother. The next day he'd written a note to the therapist—"Thank you for helping me express my feelings." She was astonished and moved.

In the Space Room, Albert decided to be his older brother Marty. His voice deepened and his body seemed to grow bigger.

"So what do you and Albert like to do together?" Malcolm asked him.

"Rough-housing, that's what I like. He squeals a lot but I don't care." Albert had told us before how he hated his brother's rough play.

"What do you think Albert wants more than anything?" I asked.

"Marty" looked thoughtful. "He wants to come home in the

summer. He wants everything to be OK by then." When his turn was over, Albert had trouble letting go of the role, cuffing and harshly teasing the others in a way that seemed unlike himself. We had to remind him two or three times—"Albert, you're Albert, remember? You're not Marty any more."

Ronnie surprised me by being able to take on another role consistently. "Hi, I'm Nicky," he said in a high voice. "I'm Ronnie's brother and I'm only three and a half." He looked convincingly like a small boy, swinging his legs under the chair and chewing on his hand.

"Do you and Ronnie get along?" asked Elizabeth.

"Well, he's always beating me up."

"How come he beats you up?"

"Because I always punch him."

"What does your mom do?"

"Sometimes she hits Ronnie and then he cries, then he beats me up again."

Kiki was last. She left the room and came back in smiling and dignified. "Hello, everyone. My name is Annabel and I'm Kiki's big sister. I'm nineteen. My job is managing a supermarket."

"Hi, Annabel. Tell us about Kiki."

"She's my favorite sister, she's very funny and I miss her. A lot. She's very smart, too. She wants to be a lawyer when she grows up." I was touched. I had no doubt that Kiki was bright enough to become a lawyer—but how was she going to get there from here? She was black, female, poor, the child of a drug addict, institutionalized for emotional disturbance at the age of nine. She would need more luck than seemed likely to come her way.

It was time to end. The role-playing exercise had taken the place of stories this session: another way to act out personal truth. Malcolm, who had a gift for sensing what the group needed, suggested a song. "How about 'We shall overcome'?" he said. All the kids knew it. They added their own words, prompted by the invitation that was in the air, to dream about the future:

"We'll have lots of money," sang Ronnie.

"We will all go home," sang Elizabeth.

"We'll grow up and be happy," sang Kiki.

"We will have nice families," sang Albert.

"There will be peace in the world," sang Malcolm, a little embarrassed but determined to say it. When the song was over he shook everyone's hand.

Albert was in trouble again in school. When Prue and I came to pick him up, his teacher was reluctant to let him go. "Albert, I just don't think you can handle it," she said.

"I can! I'll be all right! I really want to go, *please*, Carmen." At length she agreed. But as soon as he was in the Space Room he reverted to being giggly and rude. As usual, Ronnie caught his mood, and even Malcolm was affected. The girls were exasperated. Elizabeth wanted to tell us about her grandfather's death during the week. She'd gone home for the funeral. Albert tittered as she spoke and tossed a pen from his pocket across the circle to Ronnie.

"Catch!"

Ronnie caught it and tossed it back. I grabbed the pen.

"Stop!" There was silence. "Everybody breathe." They did. I waited before going on. "Albert, do you want to listen to Elizabeth? Or do you want to go back to class?"

His tension released a little by the deep breathing, Albert's hysteria was subsiding. "It's OK, I can listen. Sorry, Elizabeth. I'm sorry about your grandfather."

"It's hard to think about death," I said. "But it happens in all our families."

They all nodded. "I got something to say," said Malcolm. He paused, looking down. "I'm thinking about my cousin. The other one. John." His voice was very quiet. "He was 28 and he had three little kids, and now he's dead. I'm scared about living in the city again. My mom wants us to move somewhere safer when I go home in June."

I wanted him out of that war zone. Malcolm was a remarkable boy. The world needed the adult that he would become, if he survived.

"My grandmother died, too," said Ronnie. "I was sad, *and* I was glad, because she wasn't in pain any more and also I got to see all my relatives." He was direct, sincere; so different from the Ronnie of a few weeks ago.

"When my dad died I laughed," said Albert, hunched over his knees. "My mom told me I should cry. I didn't know what to do, because he'd been real mean to us. I'm not sorry he's dead."

I was ready for this somber theme to continue when we did a story. But Elizabeth told about a good time with her brother and cousin and friends, all of them having an uproarious water fight in the park. All of four of the other kids acted, expressive and imaginative in their assigned roles. They were a team, cohesive, disciplined, creative.

It was our last session. Elizabeth was missing, kept in class by an unrelenting teacher. Carol listened with pursed lips to our pleas—this is the last of six sessions, we think this group has been very significant for all of the children, our closure together is important—and shook her head. "You can take Ronnie, but Elizabeth's not going." It was a familiar dilemma. We wanted Elizabeth to come, for her own and everyone's sake. But forcing Carol to let her go might backfire on us later. We needed the teachers' goodwill and cooperation. Promising Elizabeth that we'd find her after school, we took Ronnie and left her sighing over the schoolwork she'd refused to do earlier in the day.

The others were disappointed not to see her. They were troubled that the group was ending and showed it by being distracted and giggly. It took them a while to settle down. We'd brought art materials for a final activity: each of them was to make a card like a book cover bearing the title of her or his life story. Inside, the rest of us would write goodbye messages.

The Space Room was quiet as the children worked, decorating their book covers with drawings and symbols. Kiki's title was *The Girl Who Wanted to be a Lawyer*. Albert wrote *Albert's History*. Ronnie, glancing over Albert's shoulder, called his book *Ronnie's Humor*. Malcolm's was *Malcolm's Adventures in Life*. They passed their "books" around. "You are a kind and good person. I will always remember your two cousins." wrote Kiki in Malcolm's. "Thanks for letting me show my feelings," wrote Albert in Kiki's. "I had fun with you and everyone," wrote Ronnie. "When we're grown up and you're a lawyer, you can help me," wrote Malcolm to Kiki. "Now I know that we have stories in our lives," he wrote to Albert.

A few weeks later I tape-recorded individual interviews with Albert, Elizabeth, and Kiki about the experience of being in the group.

One of my questions was about its duration—how did they feel about meeting for six sessions?

"It was too short," said Albert emphatically.

"*Way* too short!" said Kiki when I put the same question to her a couple of days later.

"I wish it was longer," said Elizabeth when it was her turn. "I wanted to keep coming."

"How long would you have liked it to be?" was my next question to each of them.

"A year," said Kiki.

"Maybe four months or six months," said Elizabeth.

"How long? *I* think, every single week," said Albert. "Yup, every single week, that would be better."

Eleven

SHADE SINGS HER LIFE

Shade was eight, nearly nine, when I began seeing her in individual sessions. I'd known her for two years as one of the most rambunctious of the Anthonites, a little cocoa-brown girl who looked like a boy and was always getting in trouble for her violent tantrums and corrosive language. Shade would rarely stay in the room for the duration of a group session—the staff would remove her for attacking another kid, or she would remove herself, muttering insults about this dumb-ass activity. But she'd been asking for some time to have music by herself. There was something about Shade's spirit that drew me, and I was curious to see how she would be outside the group. I knew that Shade's strong motivation meant that music therapy was likely to provide something valuable for her. What exactly it might be I would wait to find out.

Shade had been trying to look more like a girl. "Do you like my new dress?" she asked when I came to pick her up. We walked downstairs, Shade clumping along the hall in her big white shoes like a boyish Minnie Mouse. We'd already met for two sessions in which she'd explored the Space Room and its various treasures. She liked singing, but preferred to improvise her own songs rather than reprise the ones we'd sung in the group.

She picked up the guitar and strummed the open strings.

"You sing something, I'll play for you," she said.

I began making up a song in the rhythm of Shade's strumming:

Shade is a pretty girl
She's wearing a pretty pink dress

On a sunny springtime morning

Shade responded, singing her slow lines with concentration as she strummed the guitar. Her voice was hoarse, as it always was in both singing and speaking.

Jo Salas has a nice voice
Just like me, just like me
When she goes to heaven she'll be singing
When the kids bury her and sing
When she gets very old
She'll never die without the kids
And they'll never forget her when she dies
About her singing too, singing too
And what she said to me when I was only eight years old

Her song continued for ten focused minutes.

These extended impromptu songs soon became a feature of Shade's music therapy, something she chose to do consistently. She had a fluency and a capacity for introspection that I hadn't imagined from her behavior in group music sessions. Still formulating therapeutic goals for her, I realized that this opportunity to express herself in the poetic language of improvised song lyrics could be an important outlet for deeply-felt emotion.

In another session, Shade improvised at the piano for a while, her music purposeful and creative. Then she accompanied herself on a hand drum as she sang for several minutes about being a powerful person who can save lives. Her voice, meanwhile, was a feeble thread of sound.

I'd worked with several children whose emotional wounds manifested in their voices. It had sometimes been productive to work on the voice itself: creating more openness, strength or clarity in the voice helped, through the alchemy of the body-mind connection, to bring new strength to the personality. Denyse, twelve years old, loved to sing but annoyed everyone with her loud, harsh, and egregiously untuneful singing, an analogue to her abrasive behavior toward other children and staff. In music therapy sessions, feeling shy and exposed with only me for her audience, her singing voice dwindled to a tuneless whisper. Eventually—it took many weeks to build a connection with this girl, who knew only how to alienate people either with aggression or with a leech-like attachment—Denyse was able to move slowly toward more musical singing, in both intonation and the quality of her voice. She became literally more attuned: more related, with eye contact and reciprocal communication, as well as tuneful in her singing. The actual quality of her voice also changed. After a couple of years, and with frequent steps backward as well as forward, Denyse was singing in a voice that was strikingly beautiful and accurate, earning sincere praise from her formerly critical peers.

Shade's voice, in its chronic hoarseness and frequent weakness, conveyed despair and vulnerability. I wanted to work with her voice though I knew it would take a long time to know if this was a useful tactic or not.

"Shade, can you take bigger breaths when you sing?" I asked her when she paused. She did and it made a noticeable difference. She sat up straighter and her voice became stronger and clearer. Together we sang the music therapy version of "Alice's Restaurant," where you can get anything you want, anything at all. Shade filled in a line: "I want lots of money so I can see my mother." Shade was freed for adoption when she was two and had not seen her mother since she was five.

"I want to sing about Leonie leaving," announced Shade as she came into the Space Room another time. Leonie was Marilyn's popular successor as the childcare supervisor in the Anthonites. Now she was leaving to join the Peace Corps, though she talked of coming back to St Mary's afterwards. The children were bereft. Shade sang for an unbroken half hour, interspersing urgent drumming with her vocal lines:

I will miss you, Leonie
Leonie I hope you have a good time
Leonie I love you so
I hope you don't make no mistakes
I hope you come back in two years
But in two years I'll probably be eleven
Leonie I wish you could come back now
But you can't

First you went to Florida
Then you're going to go to South America
Leonie I will always remember you by the picture we have of you
Hanging up in your office

She asked me to transcribe her song so she could give it to Leonie. I had got into the habit of taping her songs, so struck was I by their expressive fluency. She herself seemed to recognize the significance of this self-expression, unduplicated, as far as I knew, by anything else in her life. Shade had found an aesthetic form to embody a deeply resonant expression of her emotion and perception. Her concentration and her consistency — always accompanying herself with open-string strumming on the guitar, or playing simple percussion — were remarkable.

I'd realized that Shade's characteristic macho walk was the result of the extraordinary tension in her body. Her neck and shoulders were so rigid that she couldn't turn her head without turning her whole upper body. It seemed likely that the radical restriction of her vocal range and the hoarseness of her voice were related to her physical tension. Shade was quite willing to experiment with breathing and relaxation and was excited to hear the dramatic change in her voice when she was able to soften her muscles even a little. The hoarseness diminished noticeably.

Shade had no contact with anyone in her family except her sister, one year older, virtually her twin in appearance. Tariqa, who was more manageable than Shade, was in a residential center that was less restrictive than St Mary's. The two girls saw each other every couple of months, visiting for a day at St Mary's or Tariqa's institution. Shade's strongest desire was to be reunited with her forever. She made up one of her bardic songs for Tariqa's birthday.

I love you Tariqa
I might be going to your party Tariqa
And I'll probably bring you a present for your birthday
I love you so much that when I visited you I didn't want to leave
    you Tariqa
Tariqa do you still want to ask your—our—foster mother

If I could come on an overnight visit Tariqa
One day I want to be like you
If only I was you and you were me
It would have been even better
If I had you as my mom
Either our foster mom or our real mom
I will live with you forever until I die
Some day I'm gonna grow like you and I'll be the same age as you,
    one day
And if you would like me and you to buy a house with our money
    when we grow up
I would appreciate doing that

The girls' most recent foster mother had ended her relationship with Shade, though not with Tariqa.

Shade sang about Tommy, her friend in the Anthonites who was about to be discharged.

If you leave me I'll cry forever, Tommy
If you leave me I'll die
I wouldn't want to be dead for a hundred years
Just like Sleeping Beauty
I'll never last that long
I might cry when I'm up in heaven
Saying "I wish I wasn't dead"
And I'd be waiting for you until you die, up in heaven
And if you leave St Mary's
I'll never know the way to your house
One day I'll be a grownup
And I'll have a department with you
When I get money

Shade spent much of another session singing variations on "You are my sunshine:" "You are my mother, my only mother, you make me happy when skies are gray" etc. Then "You are the devil, my only devil, you make me angry when skies are gray."

"You know what's really my sunshine?" she said after a while.

"Tariqa's my sunshine." She sang, "You are my sister, my only sister…."

Later, mockingly self-aware, she sang, "You are my baby, my only baby, you're only happy when you get your way."

As Christmas approached Shade's chronic physical tension grew worse. I coached her through an extended relaxation sequence but it was almost impossible for her to release her muscles. She felt soothed, though, by the chance to lie down and be still. The next session she asked to do a guided relaxation again. But again she stayed as rigid as a tin soldier.

Christmas at St Mary's was an extraordinarily fraught time: the pain of being a family-less child at holiday time was almost unbearable. From Thanksgiving to New Year's the season was marked by one crisis after another, with far more than the usual number of children on "special alert," meaning that they were in danger of hurting themselves or others and had to be in the one-to-one care of a staff member at all times. Whatever the children's habitual defenses might be, they were raised at this time, usually unsuccessfully. Shade's muscular armor was, I believed, a vain, desperate attempt to barricade her heart.

I came to get Shade from the group a couple of days after Christmas. She was in her room doing "time out" for some offense. She scowled when she saw me.

"I'm not coming to music so fuck off, dickface."

I was taken aback. I'd often heard her speak like this but not to me. "Hey, Shade," I said, staying in the doorway. "What's wrong?"

Ted, the childcare worker on duty, appeared beside me. "She can go, don't worry," he said. "It would do her good. Come on, Shade," he said to her, "you wanted to go with Jo, remember?"

She looked down, muttering inaudibly.

"She's been having a real hard time since Christmas," whispered Ted. "She thought Tariqa was coming to visit but she didn't show up."

"Shade," I said. "Let's go for a little while. We'll see what happens." She slouched to her feet, her face still clouded, and followed me to the Space Room. Once inside she became more like her usual self, at least the self that I was used to seeing in our sessions.

"I was mad," she said, drooping over the guitar and picking the strings desultorily. "Everything's been fucked up around here." We played together. She didn't sing until close to the end when she asked for a Christmas carol. Her voice was feeble and so hoarse she could hardly sing.

As the festive season retreated after the new year Shade's mood improved. "It's Ted's birthday," said Shade one day as soon as we left the group. "I want to make a card for him." We borrowed some supplies from the art therapist. Shade made a beautiful card with rainbow-colored animals and an enigmatic object like a tennis racquet. Her work was fluent and inventive and she was pleased with it when she finished.

She made up a song about how much she wanted to have a family, singing without pause for nearly fifteen minutes. We ended the session with guided relaxation again. For the first time she succeeded in fully relaxing her neck and shoulders.

Shade wanted to draw again in the following sessions, first a Valentine's Day card for Lynn, her clinical coordinator and therapist, then, a week later, a picture of Supergirl.

"Should I make her black or white?" she asked. "Supergirl is white, right? Or maybe she's part black and part white like Jana." Jana was a new girl in the Anthonites. She looked African-American but her mother, whom all the kids had met, was white.

"I think Supergirl could be anything. Why don't you make her the same as you?" I suggested.

"OK!" said Shade, coloring in Supergirl's face with a brown crayon. "Nah, she looks like shit," she said, looking it over when she'd finished.

"I think she looks good," I said.

"Yeah, maybe she's OK." She picked up the drawing and spoke to it. "You wanna be black, Supergirl?" She held it to her ear, then nodded. "She says yes."

Shade told me about fighting with Jana.

"She made me so mad, I could just kill that girl. Mean and ugly, that's how I feel about her." She knew the "Mean and Ugly" song from the group sessions and sang it now with satisfaction, a wide and wicked grin on her face. Her singing this time was vigorous and freer than usual.

"Shade, you could try singing this song up in the group when you get mad instead of yelling at people or hitting them."

"That's a good idea, Jo Salas!"

A few weeks later, drawing another picture, she mused about ideals of feminine beauty.

"Do you think this is a beautiful girl, Jo? Look at her long hair and her big blue eyes."

"What do you think?"

"I think she is. Am I pretty, do you think?"

"Yes, you are, you're very good-looking, Shade."

"Oh yes, I'm *very* good-looking." She was smiling but her tone was utterly sarcastic.

Next spring Shade began complaining about coming to music. She'd been in music therapy now for a year. After two or three occasions of agreeing to come only after angry protests I suggested that she take a few weeks off. She came back five weeks later, quite happy to be with me again. Her music that session was remarkable, a 30-minute improvisation on the drums with exquisite control and musicality. I played with her and felt the flow of her initiative and responsiveness, the unmistakable force of co-creativity. Shade looked at me when we paused, her eyes shining. "Let's do a bit more and tape it so I can show everyone in the group." I was glad to hear her well-deserved pride.

Shade's mother, out of touch for years, came for a brief visit. I saw Shade shortly afterward. She was stirred up, but thoughtful and articulate. "I want to see her again, *and* I don't want to, because I'm mad at her. She didn't come and see me since I was five years old. I don't call that a good mom, do you?" She sighed. "She was pretty, though. She looks like Tariqa." Shade didn't see how alike she and Tariqa were, and what it meant about herself if Tariqa resembled their pretty mother. She made up a song about moms who leave their small children and how she was going to be a good mother when she grew up.

In spite of her apparently measured response, Shade was deeply unsettled by her mother's reappearance. She had been going through a hard time in the group even before the visit. Over the next few weeks she became more troubled and unmanageably belligerent. At last the treatment team sent her to the children's psychiatric hospital in the hopes that the more restrictive program there would help her calm down, as it had in the past. She came back after a couple of weeks, more peaceful and glad to be "home."

Back in the Space Room again, Shade was delighted with her

fluency in improvising on the resonator bells. "I want to do this in the talent show! Will you do it with me?"

Several times a year the rec staff organized talent shows in the gym, rowdy, jolly affairs which could erupt into mayhem at any moment. I was usually hesitant about children performing a song or instrumental piece that they'd developed in music therapy, knowing that humiliation and disappointment were as likely to be the result as the satisfied pride they deserved. If the children insisted, I sometimes played or sang with them to support them though it felt to me like playing for the bloodthirsty masses in the Roman Coliseum. If the audience didn't like what you were doing it was thumbs down and no mercy.

Shade was so excited about performing that eventually I agreed to arrange it. In the talent show we set up the resonator bells for her and a set of chimes for me, and improvised together just as we did in the Space Room. Our music was minimalist and quiet compared to the amplified blare of the previous lip-syncers, dancers, and rappers. But, to my relief, the children listened. Shade played with her usual sensitivity and confidence. When we finished the applause was tumultuous. Shade smiled her wide brilliant smile, holding my hand as she bowed to the audience.

Shade was watching a science fiction movie in the Anthonite living room when I came to pick her up for a rescheduled session. I'd been out sick the previous day.

"I'm so glad you're barely alive!" she exclaimed, leaping up to hug me. As we walked downstairs she was full of questions, prompted by the movie, about the likelihood of a comet hitting the earth. I told her that experts thought something like that had happened 64 million years ago and wiped out the dinosaurs. She stopped and stared at me. "That was a diss!"

In the Space Room Shade wanted to listen to a tape of the musical "Annie." She'd spent part of each recent session listening to this tape, drawn by the theme of an orphan who finds people to love her.

Maybe when I wake
They'll be there calling me "Baby"
Maybe

She mimed an interpretation of the song as she listened, opening her arms to me as Annie wakes to her new parents. I held her.

Shade's treatment team had to make a difficult decision. The social workers had found a place for her at another institution, one where she could stay through her adolescence if need be. Shade, now almost eleven, was going to be discharged at the end of the fall semester, just before the holidays. She was not happy. Her fantasy was still to live with Tariqa. But Tariqa was leaving residential care and returning to the foster mother who no longer wanted to see Shade. In her music sessions Shade talked, drew, sang and danced her fears and sadness. She wrote songs and poems for children and staff. Lynn, her therapist, helped her take photos of all her favorite people to include in a book of mementos. I posed with Shade in the Space Room, smiling into the camera though I felt more like crying. I was afraid that the harshness of a huge institution would push this child downhill, that she would not find space there for her large and artistic soul.

It was Shade's last session. "I don't want to go," she said, her voice hoarser than ever. "Those girls at Riverstone, they hurt you, they beat you up. I feel like shooting myself." She'd expressed these fears repeatedly and I'd passed them on to the rest of the treatment team. They were concerned, but there seemed no alternative for Shade's next step. They felt it was better for her to be safely ensconced in her next placement before the predicted storms of puberty arrived.

She listened again to her favorite songs from "Annie." "She just wants her own parents, it don't even matter what they're like."

We drew pictures and exchanged them as last gifts. Shade made up one more song:

If I have to leave
My soul will crush into pieces
One day I'll miss you forever
I will never see you again

Twelve

TAMIRA'S SECOND CHANCE

We had begun a second Playback group at the same time as Malcolm and Kiki's. The children were younger, between eight and ten years old, and enthusiastic about this diversion from school.

We sat on the circle of cushions while Prue explained about the rules.

"It's pretty easy, really. No hitting, be respectful, and listen when someone else is talking." The five children nodded solemnly, familiar with such rules from school and their living groups.

Septimus raised his hand. He was a roly-poly child with an earnest expression. "And no pulling stuff out of the cushions," he said. David looked up sharply from his surreptitious digging.

"And no laughing when someone's being serious," said Tamira, a big-boned girl with huge hands and dancing eyes.

"And no eating or drinking," contributed Damon severely.

"And no looking out the window," added Paul, dapper in matching blue shirt and pants.

Prue and I looked at each other. "Well, the most important ones are about being respectful and listening and no hitting, OK?"

"OK," they agreed.

So far so good. But once we got them onto their feet and into action—doing a simple warm-up together—it was like letting the genie out of the bottle. Paul ran to the window and forced it open, screaming to the kids outside on the playground. Tamira and Septimus drummed wildly on the locked piano. David stayed on the floor, transferring his archaeological attention to loose threads in the carpet. Damon looked from one to the other like a startled rabbit about to run for cover.

"OK, everyone!" I shouted. "Back on the cushions, please!" Prue took Tamira's hands and playfully steered her back to the cushions. Tamira struggled out of her grasp. "Leave me alone!" she growled. Prue backed off. The last thing we wanted was a confrontation with Tamira in our first meeting with this group. Tamira was well known at St Mary's for her temper and her physical strength. She sank onto the floor, cursing under her breath. In a minute all the others were seated too. Relieved, I made a new suggestion.

"Let's take turns showing a feeling with your face and body, no words. Like this." I widened my eyes and covered my mouth with my fists. "Can you guess what this feeling is?"

"Scared!" shouted Tamira.

"Nervous!" called out David.

"Yes, scared in a nervous kind of way," I said. "Who wants to go next?"

"Me!" said Septimus. He folded his arms and frowned, his face stern and tight.

"Angry!" called out all the others.

Septimus shook his head. "No, I'm upset."

David went next. He scowled and punched one hand into the other.

"Ooh! Ooh! *That's* angry!" guessed Tamira.

David looked pleased. "Fooled ya! That was *nervous!*" I could see that he was sincere, as Septimus had been. They weren't trying to trick the others, though they felt gratified when the guesses were wrong.

It was Tamira's turn. She bent her head, pretending to sob into her hands, then looked up expectantly.

"Sad!" said the others in unison.

"No, that wasn't sad," said Tamira. "That was *scared.*"

Damon rocked back and forth laughing when it was his turn. "Happy!" chorused the others. But "No, I'm not happy, I'm just laughing," he said.

The staff often talked about the way conflicts arose out of the children's inability to read nonverbal emotional signals. But this activity seemed to indicate a difficulty in knowing how to show feelings rather than in reading them, unless it was in their faulty recognition of their own emotion. Whatever the reason, there was a disjuncture in every case between what they thought they were expressing and what the rest of us saw.

"Can you think of a time when you actually felt like that?" I asked. These children were younger and much more fragile than the kids in the other group. I knew they weren't ready to tell or enact a whole story. But perhaps we could safely explore brief moments from their lives.

Septimus raised his hand.

"I was real upset this morning, 'cause Joe took my new sneakers."

"Let's have Prue play you, and who's going to be Joe?" Septimus chose Paul. Paul and Prue stood up in the stage area.

"Septimus, tell each of them one thing that they could say."

"OK, Prue's gonna say 'Get off my freakin' shoes!' and Paul's gonna say 'No way!'"

"Got that, actors?"

Prue and Paul nodded.

"Let's watch."

Septimus sat forward, his body taut, his breathing shallow. Prue hunched her shoulders and rocked slightly from side to side. Paul stood with his legs apart and his arms folded.

"Get off my freakin' shoes!" yelled Prue.

"No!" yelled Paul.

Septimus leaped off the chair. "Fucker! You better give my shoes back, asshole, or you'll be sorry!" I grabbed him and tried to bring him back. "They're just acting, remember? It's not really Joe." Septimus twisted violently in my arms. "Let go of me!" My heart was sinking at the prospect of a second round of mayhem in the very first session. Prue came in close, talking softly to Septimus. She knew him much better than I did. He began to relax, though still throwing furious looks at Paul. The other kids were agitated. I made a quick decision. "Let's stop for today, and we'll come back again next week and do some more."

Tamira was enraged. "But it's not time yet, and I wanted to have a turn."

"We need to stop now, but next week…" Tamira stormed out of the room, slamming the door. Prue followed her.

"Everyone back on the cushions! Right now!" My bossy voice worked. At my side, Septimus muttered like a kettle under the boil. "Let's sing a goodbye song, OK?" Not waiting for agreement, I began:

"Bye bye, Paul, see you later, alligator. In a while, crocodile, bye bye for now." They joined in, caught by the fun of the song. Prue and Tamira came back as we were finishing. "Bye bye, Tamira," we all sang.

"I'm sorry, Jo," she said when we finished. "I just got mad. I want to come back next week, I really do."

The children lined up by the door. I winked at Prue as we began to escort them upstairs, relieved that we were ending well after all. Then David swung his sweatshirt around his head, catching Paul in the face. Prue took the wailing Paul to the nurse to inspect his eye. Discouraged and exhausted, I returned the others to their classrooms.

We met two more times with this group but it remained chaotic and unsuccessful. We concluded that doing Playback as an active participant was too hard for children so young, so unstable, and tenuous in their identity. But Tamira was heartbroken not to continue. In the thunderstorms of her moods there were occasional flashes of a far more mature and thoughtful girl. She arrived at the third session upset, swinging her fists and cursing at all of us. Upstairs in her living unit they had just distributed a shipment of new clothes and Tamira had not been given the purple bodysuit she'd coveted. Fuming, she reluctantly accepted my invitation to sit down beside me. I strummed the guitar and began singing an impromptu song about the beautiful purple bodysuit and how bad it felt not to have it. She listened, absorbed and calmer. Then she interrupted me.

"Jo, it's not about the bodysuit."

"What's it about, Tamira?"

"I just want to get out of this place. I want to go home." I changed the lyrics of my improvised song and Tamira hummed along with me.

We ventured a fragment of a story told by Damon. He chose Tamira to play his friend Jorge.

"I ain't playin' no boy!" she expostulated, but immediately changed her mind. "I'm an actor," she said, dignified, "and actors don't have a choice." She played the brief role well.

In our closing circle Tamira reached for the guitar. I gave it to her and she strummed the open strings while we all sang the goodbye song. I knew that Tamira had no home; she had been rejected first by her mother then by one foster parent after another. There was, in fact, nowhere for her to go.

Tamira beseeched us to let her join a new group several months later. This one was to be all girls, Tamira's age or older. We were dubious. Recently she'd been going from crisis to crisis, all the while growing bigger and fiercer. But I remembered the moments of sensitivity that we had seen. We agreed to include her.

The girls were all from the Teresian living unit. Their closeness of acquaintance, I knew, would make the group either unusually intimate or impossibly explosive. The pecking order was clear from the first moments in the Space Room. The boss was Selena, a compact, pretty Hispanic girl with long black hair which she tossed over her shoulder like a spirited pony. The others watched her carefully, accepting and rejecting our suggestions according to Selena's lead.

Tamira was having trouble behaving, now that she'd got her wish. We played a game in which one person repeats a simple action while another praises her lavishly. As usual in the early sessions of a group, Prue and I partnered the girls—it was too soon to let them pair off together. When it was her turn Tamira's action quickly degenerated into something that looked like wiping her bottom. I stopped.

"Tamira, you're gross!" snapped Selena. "Why can't you grow up?"

Tamira's scatological glee turned instantly to tears. "I'm sorry! I didn't mean to!" She ran out of the room, slamming the door. I continued with the other girls while Prue saw to Tamira. Ten minutes later they returned, along with Tamira's teacher Kate.

"Kate's going to stay with us for the rest of the session," explained Prue.

Kate nodded. "I'd like to help Tamira do a good job." She knew how much Tamira had wanted to come. With Kate's support Tamira enjoyed herself without lapsing out of control. I was grateful for Kate's understanding.

Selena was upset as we walked through the hallway together on our way to the next session. She pushed away tears and fixed her eyes on the ground. "What's wrong, Selena? What happened?" the other girls kept asking, crowding around her and pulling on her sleeve. Selena was silent.

"I don't know what's going on," her teacher Meg had said when we came to pick her up. She told us that Selena, not usually a violent girl, had lashed out at her without warning. Meg was more concerned than angry. "She won't say a word. If she wants to go with you, it's fine with me. Maybe she'll open up." Head down, barely audible, Selena had insisted she wanted to come.

In the Space Room we sat down on the big pillows on the floor. The other four girls glanced at each other, uneasy. "Selena, what's wrong? Why are you crying?" I tried to divert them, afraid that their insistent questions would goad her into losing control again.

At the end of the Hello song Selena was still mute, her eyes cast down. I began singing "Hold my hand." Without looking up, Selena reached out and grasped Jenny's hand. Jenny reached out to Gracie. In a few seconds everyone was holding hands. Tamira held my knee since my hands were occupied with the guitar. Some of the girls sang softly with me. Selena wept as though her heart would break.

"Selena," I said when the song was over, "would you like to tell a story? Maybe about what made you so sad?"

She looked up at last. "Yes."

In the teller's chair she leaned against me. "It was because of my home visit," she said, her silence broken at last. "I just didn't want to say goodbye to my mom and come back here. I wanted to stay with her. I hate that I have to be at St Mary's. I got really mad in class when Meg made me do my work, so I hit her."

She told us some more about the visit, the goodbye, and what happened in school. I asked Prue to play Selena. Jenny and Gracie became her mother and her teacher. Tamira acted St Mary's itself, standing on a crate and looming over the stage area. Melissa watched from the audience.

Playing this story was hard for the girls. All were separated from their own families, two of them permanently. They did it as best they could, giggling out of tension and embarrassment at some moments, crying at others. In spite of their own emotion, they'd listened carefully: their short enactment depicted accurately what Selena had described.

As she watched, Selena wiped away more tears. Her body relaxed.

"When is your next visit?" I asked when the story ended.

"Two weeks. I guess I better not hit Meg again," she said with a watery smile, "or I'll never get home."

Back in the circle of pillows, the other girls talked about their own mothers and all the goodbyes they had experienced. Selena chose a song for us to sing together. Once again, the interwoven rituals of Playback Theatre and song had held us through a difficult emotional passage.

There was a scuffle between Jenny and Gracie as they came into the Space Room a week later. "I'll kick your butt!" muttered Jenny, a tense, cautious black girl. Gracie sidled away, all too aware of her vulnerable status as the newest and youngest girl in the Teresians. Small, chunky, and smart, she constantly monitored the other girls' responses to her, calibrating her words and actions to their expectations.

When we were ready to tell stories, Gracie, still see-sawing between giddiness and tears, was quick to offer one. It was about a conflict with Jenny earlier in the day.

"I feel so, so bad, because I just want to be friends with her," she sobbed. Jenny listened stony-faced. Gracie chose actors to act out the fight that had happened in art class. Selena played Jenny, strong and generous in her acting. I kept an eye on Jenny in the audience as the scene played out. In spite of herself she became absorbed in it. At the end she couldn't help smiling. Gracie spoke to her directly.

"I'm sorry, Jenny. Please forgive me."

"It's OK," said Jenny. "I'm OK now."

We were all pleased at this spontaneous conflict resolution, but I was uneasy at the possible dangers of using the group to tell stories about here-and-now group issues with children whose behavior was so governed by their emotional wounds.

"I got a problem with Jenny," announced Selena when we picked her up from Meg's classroom for the next session. "I'm afraid we'll get in a fight in the group."

We held a little consultation with Selena and Jenny in the hallway. Jenny was sullen and subdued. Their hostility palpable but controlled, they both decided that they would be able to participate calmly. Jenny stayed very close to me and held my hand as we walked, an unusual gesture for this reserved girl.

I taught them all "Bamboo," a simple and beautiful song which they picked up quickly. Gracie and Selena learned a harmony part. The girls were thrilled at how it sounded.

"Let's make a tape of all the songs we've sung," suggested Gracie. "We could do it when we have our party." For their final session the girls had requested a "party" with refreshments. I hoped we'd last that long.

Selena wanted to tell a story. Inspired by Gracie's, her story was about her own fight with Jenny. But Selena's intention was not to apologize or make peace. Her story was an indictment of Jenny, the current scapegoat in the mercurial and merciless dynamics of the Teresians. Jenny looked stunned. Prue and I had talked during the week about the potential explosiveness of the girls telling stories about each other. Even if the stories were positively intended, the relationships were too convoluted, too volatile. In this context we couldn't be confident of guiding the interactions to a constructive outcome. With emotionally healthy children or adults, sharing opposing points of view through Playback stories was in fact a very effective route to understanding. But most of the children at St Mary's were too vulnerable to have the necessary perspective and resilience.

"Selena, we can't do stories about other members of this group. Is there something else you'd like to tell, not about anyone who's here?" Selena lost her temper and stalked out. Gracie, to show her loyalty, glared at me and left with Selena. Prue followed them.

I sat on the pillows with Jenny, Tamira, and Melissa.

"I know why we can't tell stories about each other," said Tamira soberly. "It's because it gets too confusing."

"Can I sing a song?" asked Jenny. She held the guitar, plucking the lowest string in a steady rhythm. "I wish I could go, Oh I wish I could go, to my brother's foster-mom's house, because she's nice to me," she sang, more open and passionate in her expression than we had so far seen. From what I'd heard about her history, her brother's foster-mother was the nearest thing she had to a parent. Her own mother had beaten and starved her until the law finally intervened. Tamira, whose story was equally tragic, hummed along in her rather hoarse voice, quietly so she could hear Jenny's words.

Later I was summoned up to the Teresian group. Apparently Selena and Gracie had told Angelique, the senior childcare worker, that Jenny had caused serious trouble in the Playback group. Jenny had become enraged and was now confined to her room.

"And what is all this about? We have some very upset girls here," said Angelique in her island accent, her usually friendly face severe. I tried to explain what had happened. Angelique was skeptical.

I visited Jenny, collapsed in a miserable heap on her bed. "Am I out of the club now?" she asked. She sounded defeated. I was speechless for a moment at her acceptance of blame.

"It's not a club, Jenny, it's a therapy group," I said, "and you're still part of it, if you want to be." She looked at me, her eyes full of an ageless grief that had little to do with Selena or the other girls. I felt helpless to comfort her.

Shortly before the next session all the children at St Mary's were told that Ray, a young kitchen worker, was in the hospital after a serious stroke. He was unlikely to live. The girls were shaken, somber in the imminent presence of death. Tamira, especially, was silent and still. I realized that I had never before seen her motionless.

We sang "Alice's Restaurant" — "You can get anything you want…" When it was Tamira's turn she couldn't think of anything to say. Prue, sitting beside her, encouraged her to find a phrase for the song. Tamira whispered in her ear. Prue whispered back, then said: "Tamira wishes she felt more hope." We sang it for her. Tamira seemed barely to hear it. Later Prue told me that Tamira had whispered "Can I say 'I wish I was dead'?" Prue, worried about the effect of this statement on the other girls, had rephrased it. But her bland, positive version had little meaning for Tamira.

I asked Tamira if she would like to be a teller. She shook her head, still in the grip of her despair. Melissa, a blonde girl with lumpy features in a thin face, told a story about being with her mother and her siblings on her birthday almost a year ago. "I haven't seen them much since then," she said. But this was a happy memory. I invited her to choose one of the girls as the teller's actor, the first time we had entrusted the group with this open choice. I felt it was time, that they had by now developed enough trust and cohesion in the group. Melissa chose Tamira. I held my breath. Tamira stood up, ready. To my astonishment, she played the role with striking creativity and faithfulness to Melissa's story. Her acting was confident, in an altogether different league from that of the others.

"Yeah, Tamira!" said Melissa when it was finished. She was nodding and smiling. "That's just what I did, I screamed when I saw the cake."

The story and her success in it had lifted Tamira's gloom. It was the healing she needed in that moment, to experience herself as creative and as an agent of pleasure for someone else. She was ready to tell a story herself. Like Melissa's, it was a family memory: "It's about my best foster-mom, April, and her family. I really liked her, but she's not my foster-mom any more because she got tired of waiting for me to get it together." Tamira was matter-of-fact. Rejection was a familiar experience in her life, a repeated confirmation that she was an unlovable failure. She was so used to this assessment that it was no longer distressing, at least on the surface. "This was my last visit with her. My brother Eugene was there. He's special, he's autistic." She studied the actors and chose Melissa to play Eugene.

Melissa was offended. "I don't want to be no retard," she grumbled.

Tamira jumped up from the teller's chair and went over to her. "No, you don't understand. Eugene is wonderful, he's my favorite. We all love him." She was vehement.

Melissa couldn't be convinced. Tamira chose Gracie instead. She watched her story, entirely satisfied in spite of the acting, so much less skillful than her own. I noted again how a teller's absorption created a kind of trance in which she *saw* the events and people and far-away places of the story.

Prue and I brought cookies and soft drinks to the last session. Amid a certain amount of scrapping we managed to record six songs. "I'll make copies for you all to keep," I promised. As a farewell activity we invited the girls to tell one more story, briefly, for the rest of us just to listen to. Jenny surprised us: "My story is that my papers have been accepted by the adoption agency." This was remarkable news. There was a chorus of congratulation. I hoped that there would be a family who would see the fineness of this girl and want her with them forever.

Tamira began to say something, then stopped herself. "Can I tell you later?" she asked me. Prue and I stood with her outside her classroom after we'd dropped off the others. "I wanted to thank you for letting me be in this group."

We were touched by her humbleness and her gratitude. "You were *wonderful* in the group," we told her. "Do you know that?"

Tamira looked at us, uncertain that we meant it. Success was an all but unknown experience for her.

Thirteen

"MUSIC IS CURATIVE"

I worked with Jeffrey for three years, until the day I left St Mary's. When I met him, he was a plump ten-year-old whose intense blue eyes and cherubic looks gave no hint of either his extraordinary intelligence or the demons that haunted him. He'd come first to the "chorus," a small group of girls and boys who shared a special interest in singing. Keen as they were, for each of them the struggle was to overcome their inevitable conflicts with each other enough to enjoy the music they could make together. Mandy, the youngest of the Lewis children and now a reclusive ten-year-old, was in this group, as was Denyse, earnestly applying the singing skills she'd worked on so hard in our individual sessions. Another regular member—there were several whose enthusiasm expired after a couple of sessions—was Zeb, an impossibly slender African-American boy with a droll air and a beautiful voice.

One afternoon I answered a call at my desk.

"Hello, Jo," said a confident young voice. "This is Jeffrey Schultz in the Jeromists. I heard about the chorus and I'd really like to join it. I love to sing."

I was impressed by his worldly manner. Marie, his clinical coordinator, backed up his request when I asked her about it. "Yes, he's very musical. I think it would be good for him to sing with other kids. But you should know what you're getting into. He's much more disturbed than he seems."

In the group, Jeffrey found it very difficult to cooperate with the others. He was petulant and demanding, sulking when things did not go his way, changing his mind when they did. Zeb regarded him for the most part with benign amusement but couldn't resist teasing such an easy mark. Mandy seemed oblivious, as she was to almost everything. Denyse admired Jeffrey and tried hard to make friends with him, manipulating the seating arrangements so she could sit next to him and sing the same part. But Jeffrey was ungenerous toward Denyse's inferior talent. I tried hard to find songs where each one of them could shine in his or her own way.

Meanwhile I had begun to see Jeffrey in individual sessions. Here he was free to interact directly with the music and with me, undistracted by his social shortcomings. He often chose to play the piano, jabbing the keys in a peculiar straight-fingered way until he'd spent his store of whatever malevolent or frustrated feelings he was seething with. Sometimes he'd call out a story as he played, one frightening scenario following another. Each apparent resolution turned out to be only an escalation of danger—"But! Little did they know...."

Relaxed after his violent playing, Jeffrey wanted to sing. "Let me look at your book," he asked, reaching for the thick blue folder of songs that I'd been collecting for years. He studied it with care. "What's this like?" he asked, pointing to "Heart like a Wheel." I sang it for him. "Make a note of that one," Jeffrey instructed. "Let me see the book again."

He chose several songs to learn, all in a similar vein of expressive tenderness. He learned them over two or three sessions and sang them well with his strong, flexible soprano and secure sense of pitch. He was pleased with himself. I thought we might be able to build on his natural strength in singing to help him manage the stresses of being in the chorus, where he continued to struggle with his own thin-skinned irritability. His general creativity and articulateness also led me to think that he might like to compose his own songs. But he looked blank when I suggested it. "But I don't know how to."

In the treatment team meeting they were worried about him—about his depression, his violent fantasies, about the voices he reported hearing, about the suspicion of sexual abuse by different members of his close and convoluted family, his own sexual misbehavior in the living unit where he apparently was in the habit of exhibiting himself to the other boys. I had learned that he had been in foster care as an infant before being returned to his schizophrenic mother at two years old. He'd lived with her until he was eight and had been in institutions since then. He and his mother were close, though, and Jeffrey spent frequent weekends in her company. The team shook their heads over his probable fate. "I'll up his meds a bit," said the psychiatrist, Dr Keller. "See if that helps." Jeffrey had been taking a strong anti-psychotic medication, seldom used with children, since he was nine.

I wrote a song for him about being able to depend on yourself when the adults around you are not able to help. Jeffrey learned it quickly and sang it as though he'd written it himself, ornamenting the melody and phrasing it with musical and dramatic effect.

> Sometimes I'm scared, I don't know where to go
> The people that I turn to tell me they don't know
> But I'm learning how to count on me
> Yes, I'm learning I can count on me

The second verse was about being sad, the third about being angry. After a few minutes he had the words fully memorized. He wanted to sing it several times in succession.

Christmas was coming and the chorus was practicing four songs to sing at the carol sing-along in the big living room. Jeffrey was in a torment of ambivalence.

"I'm not going to sing."

"OK, I'll sing, I really do want to."

"I quit chorus!"

And so on. When the time came he hung back and listened to the first three of our rehearsed songs, then stepped up and joined us for "The Little Drummer Boy." His clear voice rang out, blending with Zeb's deeper one and the wavering tones of Denyse and Mandy.

For a long time Jeffrey seemed to have no response to my occasional suggestions to compose something original. But one day he came into the Space Room with a decisive announcement. "I want to write a song. Here's how it goes." He began singing an upbeat little tune, developing the melodic contour as he explored it. I played a guitar accompaniment to frame and support it. "Do you want to write words for it, Jeffrey?"

We sat together on the outsize red pillow, a recent addition to the room. Jeffrey dictated lyrics to me, matching them carefully to the lines of his melody:

The bridge is falling down
You better go tell the construction worker
that the bridge, la la la la, is falling down
Down, down, down

Look, the little boy is on that bridge
you better go there and catch him
Sail under the bridge with your boat
Sail under the bridge and catch the boy

It was the first of many songs that Jeffrey was to write. I had no doubt that the imagery and mood of the song depicted important aspects of Jeffrey's inner life; but I trusted the language and music to do their work most effectively without discussion or interpretation.

In another session, Jeffrey wanted to sing with me as the "audience." I applauded enthusiastically as he strode out from behind the closet door, his MTV swagger in comic contrast to his choirboy appearance. With an elaborate flourish he put on a pair of imaginary sunglasses and embarked on one of his favorite songs:

I believe that the children are our future
Teach them well and let them lead the way
Show them all the beauty they possess inside
Give them a sense of pride...

There was enormous conviction in his presentation. It was a musical performance: he built the song, taking full account of each phrase, each pause, ending on a sustained note complete with vibrato. He paused just long enough to acknowledge the audience's thunderous applause, then gave me an instruction.

" 'Sometimes I'm Scared,'" he said. He was referring to the song I'd written for him earlier, on the theme of self-reliance in the face of other people's unpredictability. He pointed to the guitar. "You play."

I transformed instantly from audience member to accompanist.

"Again," he said when he'd finished all the verses. We did the song again. As he sang he conducted my guitar playing, gesturing me to strum loudly when we came to the verse about anger.

Jeffrey sang the song five times in succession. He said nothing about his urgency to sing it, and I saw no need to press him: the music was expression enough. It was apparent that singing these lyrics at this particular moment was helping him not only to express some core feelings but also to find relief and integration.

A few weeks later Jeffrey asked me about making a dulcimer. He'd seen the results of the kits that I'd put together with a couple of the other kids. I thought it was a good idea. We took some time in the next few sessions to work on it. Jeffrey was meticulous, making sure he understood what to do at each step.

"I think it's ready, Jeffrey," I said one day. "We just have to string it up."

He was excited. With the strings in place he strummed it delicately. "Gorgeous!" he beamed. "Can I take it to the group?"

I thought about the rough atmosphere of the Jeromist group and wondered if I should insist that it stay safely in the Space Room. But it was Jeffrey's instrument now. He took it with him proudly. The next session he was evasive, changing the subject when I asked him about it. Marie told me later that two of the other boys had destroyed it. Jeffrey had not tried to save it, swearing that he didn't care what happened to it. I knew that his role in the Jeromists was complex and tenuous; he didn't know how to take part in the streetwise jockeying for rank that went on there constantly. Being plump, white, and easily offended didn't help. I was sorry about the dulcimer, and even more about the impossibility for Jeffrey to hold onto an object that reflected a little of what was rare and wonderful about himself.

Jeffrey came into the Space Room with his shirt misbuttoned and his hair like a bird's nest. He made straight for the big pillow, curling up on it and covering himself with the piece of furry fabric that he used as a blanket at times like this. He'd just come back from a home visit and as usual was feeling shaken. By now, more than a year and a half after we'd begun working together, he'd given me a picture of a very strange household indeed, with doors and windows firmly closed against any breath of air from the outside world.

"Sing some tender songs," he said, his eyes already closed.

In spite of Jeffrey's own joy in singing, there were times when he wanted only to listen. I sang "The Rose" and some of his other favorites. He seemed comforted.

Suddenly he sat bolt upright.

"Notebook!" This was his imperious way of telling me he had a song to write. Since his first song about the boy on the bridge, Jeffrey had written many more, often coming in with a palpable urgency to get his lyrics onto paper and then into song. "I *need* music," he told me, and it was impossible to doubt it. (The treatment team had recognized that for this boy, music therapy was proving far more effective than conventional treatment. They endorsed his coming twice a week for music and allowed him to drop his sessions with the psychologist where he did nothing but sit in stubborn silence.) I'd bought a special notebook for him to write in. I had thought he might like to keep it with him in the group in case of sudden inspiration but he seemed hesitant and I didn't press it, remembering what had happened to the dulcimer.

He muttered as he wrote, pausing sometimes to chew the pen or stare at me until he found the word he wanted.

I'm so tired
And I just don't feel right
The phone was ringing left and right
Kept me up all through the night
Everybody's screaming
Everybody's angry
Seems like everyone wants to start a fight
But now it's time for me to hang up
Pull the cord out
And say goodnight

We sang it over a blues chord sequence, Jeffrey deciding the tempo and phrasing with his usual musicality. "I feel like a river," he said. "Calm and flowing."

"Do you think I could be a singer when I grow up?" asked Jeffrey a few months later. We talked about what it takes to be a professional singer, and what kind of singer he might be. "I know I can make people cry," he said. "I sang for Marie yesterday when the other kids were at the soccer game. And she cried. I have to admit I think it was the words of the song as much as my singing, though. She cares a lot about all the kids. She knows life is damn hard."

In his next session Jeffrey wrote a letter to the girl for whom he'd composed a sweet song a few weeks before. "I still say you are an amazing girl even though you hurt my feelings," he wrote. "You will like me when you get to know me better. I believe I have a good personality and I am one of the most dignified kids at St Mary's. I have learned to like myself, including the way I look."

He folded it carefully and put it in his pocket. "Let's sing 'Heart Like a Wheel'," he said. But he stumbled over the words and seemed to have difficulty coordinating his breathing. I'd occasionally noticed an odd hesitation in his singing but it had never before been bad enough to stop him. "I think it's my medication," he said, giving up in frustration. I didn't know what to think.

Jeffrey was distraught when he came in next. "You play," he said. " I just want to listen." I improvised on the piano while Jeffrey sat with his head in his hands, the picture of sorrow. "Stop, Jo," he said after a few minutes. He sat down at the synthesizer and began playing loud, harsh discords, hitting the keys with his chin and elbows, breaking sometimes to flap his hands. I waited. Abruptly he got up from the keyboard and wrote something on a piece of paper. "Stick it on my back," he said. The note said *"KICK ME"* in large uneven letters.

"Jeffrey, what's the matter?"

"Nothing."

"Did you give Samantha the letter?"

"I ripped it up, if you really want to know."

He played and sang despondently for another twenty minutes but he didn't feel better.

The treatment team was alarmed about Jeffrey's slurred speech. He was also developing tics, twitching his shoulders and jerking his head. I told them about his difficulty in singing. There were anxious glances around the table. They were afraid that Jeffrey had developed an irreversible neurological syndrome as a result of the anti-psychotic medication. "We'll take him off everything and see what happens," said Dr Keller. "It's too late!" snapped Marie. Her eyes were dark with anger.

But to everyone's relief, Jeffrey's symptoms did abate to some degree when the medication was stopped. There was also no dramatic reappearance of the psychosis that it had supposedly been controlling. He continued to have fluctuations of mood, including a suicidal depression severe enough to keep him on special alert for several weeks. Throughout this period he came to music three times a week, sometimes playing the drums and keyboards savagely until he'd spent his passion, other times singing or listening to me sing his favorite "tender" songs.

The Jeffrey I had known now for two and a half years was not psychotic, nor, as far as I could tell, moving in that direction. On the contrary, as he grew older, the great strength he'd found in himself as a maker of music seemed more and more available to him outside the Space Room. "You know, I think of you when I'm at home," he remarked once. "Then I remember about being a singer and a composer myself." His music was the expression of what was healthiest in him, and he was allowing others to see it. He now sang easily for other people: for the annual Christmas sing-along he composed a short but beautiful song which he sang solo, then invited the others to sing with him. I watched him, remembering how hard it had been for him two Christmases ago just to sing in the chorus. He also agreed, with pleasure, to submit some of his lyrics for publication in a collection of children's poems. One he'd written in a contemplative mood a few weeks back. It included the line "Music is curative." "*Curative?*" I queried. I was writing it down to his dictation and I wasn't sure I'd heard right. But I had.

Music is fine
Music is curative
Music is fundamental
Music is something you can never forget
Music is special
Music is a song
Music is something you do all day long
Music is love
Music is here

Fourteen

CODA

The time came, eventually, for me to move on to other horizons, and eventually to the work I do now, performing and teaching Playback Theatre around the world. It was not easy to leave these extraordinary and courageous young people. I knew I would never forget them. Nor would I forget what I had repeatedly observed in our work together: how the children found expansiveness and expressiveness in making music or theatre, even—or especially—those who were badly wounded by trauma; the natural growth of a young artist's healthy pride in creating something new and beautiful and meaningful; the capacity to build connection and attachment through the arts in spite of a history of painful, disappointing, or dangerous relationships; the children's ability to find satisfaction in telling their stories, seeing them enacted, and acting stories for others; the inherent rewards of working as a team; the reassurance and hope that they found in the innate purposefulness and organization of any art form.

It had also become clear to me that artistic experience was not enough to heal all wounds, however much I might want it to. I had witnessed with sorrow the inexorable deterioration of children like Lizzie or Billy whose mental illness seemed beyond cure. But with these children, as with the others who were more fortunate, the arts became a place, unreplicated in other areas of their lives, where they had a chance to experience their genuine creativity and capacity for connection. For them, as for all human beings, the experience and validation of one's individual humanity is of profound value in itself, separate from the question of whether or not mental health is restored. It is a fundamental right often taken for granted by those who have not been dehumanized by oppression, chronic illness, institutionalization, or other misfortune.

It was painful to tell the children that I was going. I had seen them so often torn by goodbyes, and now I would be another in the dispiriting series of adults who disappeared from their lives. I regretted, too, having to leave my friends and allies on the staff, particularly those with whom I'd shared a commitment to build a creative environment at St Mary's.

I made sure that the children heard directly from me, not second- or third-hand from other children or staff. There would still, of course, be a number of weeks in which to try to address whatever sorrow or anger or guilt was stirred in them. Some of the children were philosophical; others, more attached to me, were devastated. "I feel like someone stabbed me in the heart," said Jeffrey when I told him. Our last sessions were spent finding musical and verbal expression of his sense of loss and his vision of a creative future life. He himself was to leave soon: now almost thirteen, he had been placed at a home for older children, a little closer to his family. He was looking forward to it.

The art therapist—a master craftsperson in her life outside St Mary's—made an exquisite glass box and presented it to me on my last day, filled with pieces of handmade paper on which children had written farewell wishes:

"I will miss you. I will never forget the songs that you taught me. Come back soon."

"I wish you have a Happy. At your job. I hope they respect you OK. From best friend."

"Good luck Jo Salas. I wish you can stay."

"Dear Jo, I am a very shy person. I wish you good luck."

"I wish you a successful life."

"I wish she wouldn't leave."

"I wish you happenys."

I left at a time when some of the gains that we'd made in bringing the arts to St Mary's had been reversed, with the administration citing budget constraints. I wasn't confident about the future of the creative arts therapies at this institution. Over the years of my tenure, I and the other arts-minded people had slowly, arduously convinced some of the skeptics on the staff that what we were offering was a worthwhile complement to other forms of treatment. Other staff members needed no convincing, offering their respectful interest and support all along. But there remained a strong element of mistrust. The effectiveness of any therapeutic approach is hard to prove in a measurable way, and the arts therapies, with their call to the unpredictability of imagination and their basis in a humanistic understanding of life, present particularly difficult challenges. What would constitute proof that that arts therapies work? How could we ever demonstrate beyond a doubt that positive change in a child was due to her or his experience in music or drama or art? How could we convince someone that experiencing achievement and connectedness was valuable even when it did not lead to a permanent overall improvement, as with some of our most disturbed children?

We tried. We told the stories of what happened in our sessions; we showed colleagues the music and poetry and paintings that the children created; we brought attention to the small but significant increments of trust and self-esteem that stemmed from what the children did as artists; we tried to maintain our own conviction about what we witnessed every day. It sometimes felt like an uphill struggle.

The tenuous position of the arts in treatment at St Mary's and elsewhere echoes the place of the arts in education and in society in general. It is the fate of the arts to dwell uncomfortably on the fringes, at least in modern Western materialist culture. The discomfort is felt by both the arts-minded and by those in the uncomprehending mainstream who see that the arts, even when not understood and not embraced, will simply not disappear. Like the St Mary's critics, some will accuse the arts of being a waste of time, an indulgence, unprofitable, subversive, even dangerous. It is true that genuine art cannot be utilitarian or inherently profitable. In spite of that, it is still yearned for and practiced, against all odds. It is, evidently, a human need, both individually and collectively.

Every one of the palpable benefits that came to the St Mary's children through involvement in the arts is felt also by "normal" children and adults who engage in the arts as artists or audiences. Schools with the vision and the resources to provide art, music, drama, and so on see the results in a more vibrant, cohesive, and academically successful school culture, as well as in the individual wellbeing of young people who may shine first in one of the arts rather than in an academic area. Howard Gardner and other theorists have written compellingly about the need to acknowledge and serve artistic intelligences as well as more commonly recognized modes of learning. Arts education visionaries are now calling for creativity to be added to the traditional educational priorities of literacy and numeracy. A declaration by the first UNESCO World Arts Conference, held in Lisbon in March 2006, speaks of "the political and professional will to integrate the arts into an effective 'education for all', as vital instruments for learning human rights, responsible citizenship and inclusive democracy." When an educational commitment to the arts is further reflected throughout a whole community or even a nation, everyone reaps the benefits: the increased richness and solidity of civic life; a sense of shared identity and pride; and, most of all, the ongoing, vital contribution of creativity at all levels of endeavor and decision-making.

I had no idea then of the lasting harvest that would grow from the seeds we all planted for years with such insistent hope. Now, years later, St Mary's employs a full-time music therapist and art therapist — the latter working full-time in the clinical department. A new building houses a permanent gallery for the children's art. Students from a local arts-oriented college spend time on artistic projects with the children. The arts, it appears, have become part of this institution's core.

As I finished writing this book I returned to St Mary's for a visit. It was Awards Day, when every child receives an award for achievement during the school year — some for "Most Cheerful" or "Best Attitude," others for more academic distinctions. There were awards for art and music, an innovation since my time. The children I had known were long gone, now young men and women living their lives, some successfully in the community, others in institutions, shelters, or other shadowy corners. Each year two or three of them returned for Awards Day. I was glad to see Denyse, who'd spent many sessions in the Space Room learning to find her real voice. She looked exactly the same and reported that she was doing well. I asked her if we could talk by phone later, thinking that I could perhaps interview her for this book. She readily agreed, but when, a few days later, I called the number she gave me, I reached her long-estranged father. He knew only that she was living in a shelter with her two small children, and asked me anxiously how she seemed. He couldn't imagine why Denyse had given me his telephone number. I felt troubled by her evasion. Her "I'm doing really well" may have been more bravado or desire than truth. (I did, however, speak on the phone to Billy Gaston, who sounded like his old exuberant self and was delighted to be in touch. Sadly, his life had continued to be shaped by his mental illness. He'd spent years in a psychiatric hospital but had recently been released to a half-way house. He told me, with great pleasure and pride, that he was hosting a radio program and he still played the piano.)

The awards ceremony under the big tent began and ended with beautiful singing by a much larger and more accomplished chorus that I had led. Thirty-five children sang of peace, their eyes locked on the music therapist conductor, their voices sweet and strong. They were followed by a steel drum band. A young girl, her arms fragile in transparent sleeves, played an energetic solo to resounding applause. The visual arts were thriving too, with a new gallery devoted to the children's artwork. Guests were urged to visit the "Cultural Fair" in another building where children's art and craft projects were on display.

These children were not the ones I'd known so well in my time at St Mary's. And yet they were similar in their troubled backgrounds, their longing for love and security, their potential as human beings; and similar, too, in their capacity to grow and change in the discovery of their birthright as artists.

ABOUT THE CREATIVE ARTS THERAPIES

In the twentieth century, with the development of psychology as a defined discipline, the arts therapies—principally music, drama, art, dance—grew out of the recognition of art's unique capacity to inspire and connect. Beginning in the 1940s, in the U.S., Europe, and other countries, artists and clinicians together began to apply the inherent qualities of the arts to therapeutic goals. By now a substantial body of theory, research, and practice has accumulated, with training programs at universities, professional associations granting licenses and monitoring standards, and professional journals reporting on case studies and research. In the USA there are over 15,000 registered creative arts therapists working with people in hospitals, treatment centers, schools, homes for the elderly, outpatient clinics, hospices, and other settings.

Each of the individual arts therapies builds on the specific phenomena of the art form itself, organized and applied within the sheltering frame of a relationship between therapist and client or group. Arts therapies techniques themselves may operate within various theoretical frameworks ranging from psychodynamic to behavioral approaches. The majority, perhaps, base their work in a humanistic approach which values the here-and-now process of the work as an unfolding of the client's innate potential for growth and self-awareness. Many creative arts therapists are eclectic, drawing on different frames of reference as they find appropriate.

MUSIC THERAPY
Music therapy is based on the elements of music: rhythm, melody,

timbre, harmony, pace, tempo, pattern, and the intrinsic presence of order and form in music. Self-expression, communication, and integration—central goals of most forms of therapy—take place within an artistic medium that is in itself integrated, expressive, and communicative.

Music therapists work with adults, adolescents, and children with physical and mental handicaps, psychiatric disorders, emotional disturbance, medical crises, or addictions. They may work with the elderly, or people who are dying, or with their families, or with normally-functioning people seeking self-awareness and growth. The method and techniques that a music therapist chooses will depend on the needs, capabilities, and musical interests of her clients, as well as on her own musical and therapeutic background. A music therapist working with elderly women in a nursing home may play songs from the era of their young womanhood. As the women hear the familiar melodies, they recall the lyrics, they remember long-lost images of their past, their breathing deepens and they speak or sing words which are otherwise inaccessible to them. Another therapist, working individually with a patient in a psychiatric hospital, may offer an inviting selection of percussion instruments—drums, shakers, a xylophone. The patient and the therapist improvise together, communicating emotion and energies that cannot be put into words.

Music therapy can mean instrumental improvisation, composition, singing, or learning an instrument, with the emphasis on the process rather than the result. Clients might talk about how a popular song connects to their own lives, adapt lyrics to reflect their own feelings, or write full-fledged original songs. Most music therapy is based on active music-making rather than listening, though a branch of music therapy has developed a systematic use of recorded music to stimulate and guide mental imagery (Guided Imagery in Music, or GIM, created by Helen Bonny).

The experience of creativity and mastery is a powerful step in building self-esteem, an important goal for many music therapy clients. Creating a musical piece, learning to sing a song, or simply producing a drumbeat at the right moment may lead to a sense of affirmation and pride. The individual in therapy may discover an unsuspected musical affinity, particularly valuable for someone who has believed himself without talent of any kind. Whether a client is especially gifted or not, it is the therapist's task to frame musical activities so that they will be successful and satisfying, from the chromosomally-damaged three year-old breaking into a crooked smile as he hits the tambourine to the opera singer recovering from a stroke who finds the courage to try her voice again.

DANCE AND MOVEMENT THERAPY
Dance therapy (sometimes called movement or dance/movement therapy) was first developed in the 1940's, building in part on the discoveries of modern dance in the earlier part of the twentieth century when Isadora Duncan and other dancers explored aesthetic movement to express the inner self, in contrast to formal choreography. Marian Chace, a dancer who worked with psychiatric patients, was the first pioneer of dance therapy, which is based on the realization that personality, emotion, and personal history are literally embodied in our physical selves and expressed in the way we move. The neurological and biochemical dimensions of body, movement, and emotion can be accessed directly through movement, opening possibilities for healing change.

Fundamental to any healthy identity is body image, the sense of one's body in space, its shape and its boundaries. Emotionally wounded people often lack an accurate or positive body image. Dance therapy can help clients to build or heal their body image, paving the way for further growth through movement toward expressiveness, confidence, connectedness, and other therapeutic goals. Body image and movement style may be reflected to the client in a mirroring technique, helping that person to grow in her sense of who she is and how she presents herself to the world. The nonverbal nature of dance also allows a safe but potent expression of emotion, an integral goal for many adults and young people.

Dance therapists, like other arts therapists, have the entire repertoire of the art form to draw on: improvisational movement to music; simple choreographed structures created by either the therapist or the client; dance steps from different cultures; solo or group movement; performance pieces; and so on. Working with a group of learning-disabled teenagers, one dance therapist created a very simple structure of four steps which, over time, became an expansive and flexible container in which the young people found security, individual expression, creativity, enduring pride, and the development of important social skills. Another therapist encouraged a group of battered women to experiment with bolder, stronger movements, knowing that the kinesthetic experience of strength would support them in standing up more effectively to their abusers.

ART THERAPY

Art therapy invites clients to translate inner perceptions and experiences into the tangible form of painting, drawing, sculpture, collage, and so on. With a full spectrum of artistic media at hand, an art therapist might show a client how to use different media, then offer support and encouragement as he or she creates works of art. Depending her theoretical orientation and the client's developmental and emotional state, the art therapist might offer interpretations of the meaning of the client's work, or invite the client to ponder his own understanding of what he has created; or encourage an increasingly fluent and creative self-expression with little or no focus on symbolic content. As in any therapy, the evolving relationship between therapist and client is significant whether it is explicitly explored or simply noted. Art therapy most often takes place in individual sessions. Group sessions offer the opportunity for exploring relationship, communication, and cooperation with others.

Art therapy in the US was first developed in the 1940s by Margaret Naumburg, a teacher who began to explore the therapeutic implications of art with children at a school based on psychoanalytic principles. She and others were influenced by the new ideas in progressive education coming from Montessori, Piaget, and others which stressed the importance of free expression of imagination, and by modern art education where, for the first time, Viktor Lowenfeld and others proposed a developmental theory of children's art and related it to intellectual growth. From the beginning, art therapy—more than the other creative arts therapies—drew heavily on Freudian and Jungian theory, because of both Freud's and Jung's attention to symbols and their visual representation. Another art therapy pioneer, Edith Kramer, stressed the importance of artistic activity as sublimation—the idea that art therapy helps people by allowing them to translate painful or problematic feelings and impulses into constructive aesthetic form instead of hurting others or themselves. The debate between the relative importance of the interpretation of the client's visual symbolic language (whether by the therapist or the client) and art as sublimation has continued as a central dialectic in the world of art therapy. Since the 1970s, as in other creative arts therapies, humanistic, existential, and transpersonal perspectives have entered the field, introducing art therapy practices based on the healing qualities of creativity itself and the belief that human beings will naturally grow toward health in a climate of acceptance and inspiration.

DRAMA THERAPY

More recently developed than the other arts therapies, drama therapy as a distinct discipline emerged in the 1960s and 1970s as a departure from the long-established practice of psychodrama. Psychodrama, created by the Austrian psychiatrist J.L. Moreno in the 1920s and developed further in collaboration with Moreno's wife Zerka Moreno, helps people relive a problematic moment from current or early life, searching for its deepest roots and exploring creative solutions in action. Although Moreno's ideas originally grew out of his passionate convictions about the nature of theatre itself, psychodrama evolved away from spontaneous performance witnessed by an audience towards a more purely clinical application. Psychodrama is now widely used in psychiatric hospitals as a method which can have a profound impact in a short time.

Over the past thirty years, drama therapy has developed as a system of treatment based in the power of theatre itself in all its forms, including performance. Renée Emunah, one of the founders of drama therapy, says "in drama therapy one begins by *acting* rather than by *reenacting*" — the therapist helps people to draw on and cultivate their creativity, as in the other arts therapies. Role play and role training are fundamental in most drama therapy. Drawing on the idea that personality consists of a constellation of roles, drama therapists may help clients to explore the different roles in their lives, from those of parent, worker, lover, and so on, to roles on the level of metaphor and archetype — angel, or pig, or the thawing earth. Depending on therapeutic goals as well as the therapist's mode of work, clients in a drama therapy session may delve into the manifestations of a symbolic role, or practice new and better ways to fulfill a social role, often in the company of other group members who play the supporting roles in each other's lives or psyche. Since drama therapy often takes place in groups, members are constantly practicing how to be with others more cooperatively and creatively, growing in self-awareness as they do so. In some situations, a drama therapist may use a problem-solving approach, enacting a troublesome scenario then inviting group members to explore alternative responses in action.

Drama therapists may guide clients to create and take part in actual performances, whether in the shelter of a hospital ward or with a public audience. But the emphasis is always on the process itself—the content of the piece that is chosen or developed, the group interactions and relationships in collaboration and rehearsal, the individual client's responses to the challenges of performance. The artistic goals of the performance remain in service to the therapeutic goals.

As with the other arts therapies, drama therapy draws on the whole vocabulary of the art form. Drama therapists use drama games, masks, puppets, improvisation, fairy-tale enactments, scripted plays, video, and more. It's also common to include other arts therapies—music, dance, art—to supplement or stimulate the work.

PLAYBACK THEATRE AS A CREATIVE ARTS THERAPY

Playback Theatre, where personal stories told by audience or group members are enacted on the spot, is not in itself a therapeutic modality. It was first developed by Jonathan Fox with myself and others as an artistic means of celebrating experience and building understanding between people, in a wide variety of community and arts settings including theatres and schools. Playback Theatre is considered to be a form of drama therapy *only* when it is used in clinical contexts by a therapist (as was the case with the work I describe in this book). Playback was early recognized for its inherent healing qualities, especially by psychodramatists and drama therapists who already knew the power of theatre to stir memory, emotion, and creativity. Alongside its development as an art form and a community resource, Playback Theatre soon grew as a method to work with adults and children with mental illness or other special needs. In clinical contexts, Playback shares many of the precepts and practices of both psychodrama and drama therapy. One distinction, though, between Playback Theatre and psychodrama in particular, is Playback's attention to all human stories including those that are joyful or revelatory: the healing is considered to come as much from bearing public witness and being truly heard as from the content of the enacted story itself.

Playback Theatre for therapeutic purposes can take place in performances, with a trained team enacting stories for an audience; or in therapy groups, where one or two trained Playback leaders create an environment in which clients themselves can become actors in each other's stories. In both performances and therapy groups, participants find affirmation in the opportunity to tell one's story in a respectful, accepting environment; the recognition that others may have had similar experiences, no matter how painful or isolating; the new light that can be shed on an old quandary when a group of people bring their fresh creativity to enacting it; the catharsis that can come from laughter or tears.

Playback Theatre therapy groups, additionally, can help clients to access the same things that have allowed so many Playback practitioners to become stronger, more generous, more creative in their own lives: the chance to spread your wings in playfulness and the discovery that you, even you, can bring healing to someone else when you act out his story. If your life has taught you that you are nothing but a failure and a burden on others, it can be deeply salutary to realize that your creativity has helped someone else.

The presence of ritual in Playback Theatre plays a fundamental role in its success as a therapeutic method. Inspired from the beginning by the role of ritual and ceremony in the community life of traditional societies, Playback Theatre, whether in performance or group settings, takes place within a strong, supple framework composed of several elements: the simple but formal arrangement of the stage; the repeated protocol of eliciting and enacting a story, the attentiveness and openness of the performers; and the leadership of the conductor, communicating with her words and her presence a sense of both safety and the unknown or the transcendent. In this framework the stories of real lives are told and remembered.

REFERENCES AND RESOURCES

CREATIVE ARTS THERAPIES:

Kenneth Aigen, *Paths of Development in Nordoff-Robbins Music Therapy.* 1998.Gilsum, NH: Barcelona Publishers.

Kenneth Bruscia, *Case Studies in Music Therapy.* 1991.Gilsum, NH: Barcelona Publishers.

Renee Emunah, *Acting for Real: Drama Therapy Process, Technique, and Performance.* 1994. New York: Brunner/Mazel.

Jonathan Fox, Ed., *The Essential Moreno: Writings on Psychodrama, Group Method, and Spontaneity by J.L. Moreno.* 1987. New Paltz, NY: Tusitala.

Robert Landy, *Persona and Performance: The Meaning of Role in Drama, Therapy, and Everyday Life.* 1993. New York: Guilford Press.

Fran Levy, Ed., *Dance and Other Expressive Therapies.* 1995. New York: Routledge.

David Read Johnson and Penny Lewis, Eds., *Current Approaches in Drama Therapy.* 2000. Charles C Thomas.

M.B. Junge with P. P. Asawa, *A History of Art Therapy in the United States.* 1994. Mundelein, Il: American Art Therapy Association.

Shaun McNiff, *Art as Medicine: Creating a Therapy of the Imagination.* 1992. Boston: Shambhala.

Clive Robbins and Paul Nordoff, *Creative Music Therapy.* 1977. New York: John Day.

Judith Aron Rubin, *The Art of Art Therapy.* 1984. New York: Brunner/Mazel

S. Sandel, S. Chaiklin, and A. Cohn, Eds., *Foundations of Dance/Movement Therapy: the Life and Work of Marian Chace.* 1993. Columbia, MD: American Dance Therapy Association.

PLAYBACK THEATRE:

Jonathan Fox, *Acts of Service: Spontaneity, Commitment, Tradition in the Nonscripted Theatre.* 1994. New Paltz, NY: Tusitala.

Heinrich Dauber and Jonathan Fox, Eds., *Gathering Voices: Essays on Playback Theatre.* 1999. New Paltz, NY: Tusitala.

Jo Salas, *Improvising Real Life: Personal Story in Playback Theatre.* 1993. New Paltz, NY: Tusitala.

Performing Playback Theatre: training DVD co-produced by the School of Playback Theatre and Hudson River Playback Theatre. 2006: New Paltz, NY.

EDUCATION:

Alfie Kohn, *Punished By Rewards: The Trouble with Gold Stars, Incentive Plans, A's, Praise, and other Bribes.* 1993. New York: Houghton Mifflin

Howard Gardner, *Frames of Mind.*1983. New York: Basic Books

Maxine Greene, *Releasing the Imagination: Essays on Education, the Arts, and Social Change.* 1995. San Francisco: Jossey-Bass.

Christopher Small, *Music, Society, Education.* 1977. London: John Calder.

Christopher Small, *Musicking: The Meanings of Performing and Listening.* 1998. Hanover, NH: University Press of New England.

OTHER:

Judith Herman, *Trauma and Recovery.* 1992. New York: Basic Books.

Rollo May, *The Courage to Create.* 1975. New York: Norton.

Oliver Sacks, *The man who mistook his wife for a hat.* 1987. New York: Harper and Row.

FOR PROFESSIONAL ASSOCIATIONS, JOURNALS, AND TRAINING INFORMATION, CONTACT:

International Playback Theatre Network: www.playbacknet.org

Centre for Playback Theatre: www.playbackcentre.org

American Music Therapy Association: www.musictherapy.org

National Association of Drama Therapy: www.nadt.org

American Art Therapy Association: www.arttherapy.org

American Dance Therapy Association: www.adta.org

SONG REFERENCES:

"Four Strong Winds." Ian Tyson. Published by Warner Bros. Inc., 1963.

"The Rose." Amanda McBroom. Published by Warner-Tamerlane Publishing Corp, Hollywood; Allstar & Third Story Music Inc., 1977.
"Love somebody." Joan Whitney and Alex Kramer. Bourne, Co. Publisher.
"We shall overcome." Zilphia Horton, Frank Hamilton, Guy Carawan, and Pete Seeger. Published by Ludlow Music, 1960 and 1963.
"The Carnival is Over." T. Springfield and F. Farian. Published by Chappell & Co. Inc.
"Greatest Love of All." Linda Epstein and Michael Masser. Published by EMI Golden Torch Music Corp.
"A Change Comes Over Me." Dillon Bustin, from Dillon Bustin's Almanac, June Appal Records.
"Maybe." From *Annie*. Lyrics by Martin Charnin.

All other quoted songs are in the public domain or composed by the author.

Author's note: Song lyrics and poems spontaneously created by children during therapy sessions have been quoted verbatim from my notes and audiotapes. I ask any readers who might recognize quoted lyrics as their own to contact me, either with retroactive permission to print their words, or a request not to include them in future printings of this book.

With thanks to the WG's.

CPSIA information can be obtained
at www.ICGtesting.com
Printed in the USA
LVHW111525181219
640938LV00003B/425/P